The Thirteenth Book of *Sunday Times* Crosswords

Edited by Barbara Hall

with Solver's Guide by Elizabeth and Derek Jewell

D0800045

TIMES BOOKS
A Division of HarperCollinsPublishers

Published by
Times Books
A Division of HarperCollins*Publishers*
77–85 Fulham Palace Road
Hammersmith
London W6 8JB

Copyright © The Sunday Times 1994

Typeset by Tradespools Ltd, Frome
Printed and bound in Great Britain by
HarperCollins Book Manufacturing, Glasgow

ISBN 0 7230 0593 1

The publishers acknowledge gratefully the contribution of
David Akenhead in the preparation of this book.

Also from Times Books
The Times Quiz Book
The Sunday Times Book of Answers
The Second Book of *The Sunday Times* Concise Crosswords
The Third Book of *The Sunday Times* Concise Crosswords
The Tenth Book of *The Sunday Times* Crosswords
The Eleventh Book of *The Sunday Times* Crosswords
The Twelfth Book of *The Sunday Times* Crosswords
The Fourth Book of *The Times* Concise Crosswords
The Fifth Book of *The Times* Concise Crosswords
The Sixth Book of *The Times* Concise Crosswords
The Seventh Book of *The Times* Concise Crosswords
The Fifteenth Book of *The Times* Crosswords
The Sixteenth Book of *The Times* Crosswords
The Seventeenth Book of *The Times* Crosswords
The Eighteenth Book of *The Times* Crosswords
The Nineteenth Book of *The Times* Crosswords
The Times Book of Jumbo Crosswords
The Second Book of *The Times* Jumbo Crosswords
The First Book of *The Times* Jumbo Concise Crosswords

Contents

FOREWORD

The first *Sunday Times* crossword puzzle appeared in the newspaper in January, 1925. Since then it has enjoyed continuous popularity and is reprinted in other newspapers throughout the world.

The cryptic crossword was firmly established as a national and international pastime when, over fifty years ago, the compiler of this book of puzzles began her career as a professional crossword compiler. I was then a young Wren serving with the Royal Navy in the Second World War, and working with codes.

Since those days, cryptic crosswords have become increasingly complex, with setters vying to devise new ways of word-juggling to tantalise and baffle. Would-be-solvers new to cryptics will find helpful the detailed Solver's Guide at the beginning of this book.

A good crossword puzzle must keep abreast of the times as well as being both challenging and entertaining. Each year, newly minted words swell our already enormous English vocabulary. New technical terms, too, can tax those who have not truly encyclopaedic knowledge. But all words in these puzzles can be tracked down in a good dictionary – we recommend *Collins English Dictionary* as an aid to temporarily baffled readers.

Barbara Hall

The Solver's Guide

1 SEVENTY YEARS OF CROSSWORDS

There are crazes and crazes. For a few brief months (occasionally, years) people wiggle in hula-hoops, loop the loop with yo-yos, enter marathon dance contests, bounce about on pogo sticks. The vogue hits a peak, then fades.

Well over a half a century ago, it was thought that the crossword would be simply a craze, too. It was not. It has flourished, grown into all kinds of exotic forms, and arguably become the most enduring armchair game (if game it can be called) of our century. Its combination of mental stimulation, agony, entertainment and challenge is unique.

Crosswords are tradition. Crosswords are respectable. Crosswords have been called the opiate of the eggheads. Some crosswords, the very tantalizing and intellectual ones, may be. But they are surely more than that. Heaven knows precisely how many millions of human beings around the world attempt to solve a crossword every day. There is, however, some evidence about that. During the 1960s, a Gallop poll showed that crossword solvers in the USA numbered upwards of 30 million adults, beating bridge, bingo, chess, poker and checkers as that nation's most popular leisure-time activity. Of the thousands of daily and weekly newspapers in Britain and the USA, it's unlikely that more than one per cent go to press without a crossword. On the rare occasions that publications have tried to leave out their puzzles, howls of rage have arisen from their readers. During the Second World War, British newspapers were cut back to a mere four pages – but the crosswords stayed.

Is there, indeed, a more striking example of an Anglo-American 'special relationship' than the crossword puzzle? The first one appeared on Sunday 21 December 1913 in the old New York *World* (they called it a Word-Cross Puzzle), but the man who composed it, Arthur Wynne, was born in Liverpool, England. The idea didn't reach England till eleven years later, since when the two countries have vied to make bigger, better and more idiosyncratic puzzles.

It isn't, however, an Anglo-American monopoly. In Italy in 1955 there was a plea by one Dr Michele Quitadamo for crosswords to be made part of the school curriculum. 'Crosswords', he said, 'are a valuable form of gymnastics for the intelligence.' In October 1944 Paris newspapers stopped publishing crosswords for a time for fear they might be used to convey information to the Germans. In 1966, a lady in Fiji wrote to *The Times* to say she had just completed the puzzle published in the paper on 4 April 1932: her mother had begun it and she, finding the issue years later, had finished off the job. A Serbo-Croat crossword, with 40,000 squares and 8,469 clues (compiled by one Zvonko Janah), is claimed to be the biggest ever created, although there's rather firmer evidence about the effort of Mr Robert Stilgenbauer of Los Angeles, whose 3,185-clues-across – 3,149-clues-down puzzle took him years of spare time before publication in 1949. Despite the 125,000 copies distributed, no all-correct solution has been returned! The British educational weekly, *The Teacher*, received a congratulatory letter in 1971 from the Zambian High Commission. 'Several of us have been trying to fill in these crosswords ourselves,' it reads, 'but are not of sufficient calibre to finish them – yet.'

Still, it's in the English-speaking (or, should one say, English-and-American-speaking) world that the anecdotes grow thickest. Addiction to crosswords has been compared with eating peanuts, black coffee, opium, the detective story and self-flagellation. We like the story about Mr Ronald Knox who always gave up doing *The Times* daily crossword during Lent, as a penance. This particular crossword has been mentioned in plays, books and movies. (Very true. We were rewatching that old Noël Coward weepie *Brief Encounter* on TV one night, and there was Celia Johnson's boring but steadfast old husband doing his *Times* crossword and asking her to help him with it whilst she was sitting there dreaming only of her lover, Trevor Howard. Is that unfair to crossword addicts?) It's been quoted in the law courts as a standard against which the intelligence of witnesses has been judged. A puzzle a day has been prescribed by at least one doctor – and headshrinkers are always getting in on the act. A New York psychologist believes crosswords are popular because they are 'orderly', in contrast to the disorderly world facing the crossword buff beyond. 'Here is one problem he *can* solve himself.' People work out crosswords, says a psychiatrist, for the same reason children dismantle dolls or clockwork toys, or men explore space; they want to discover what goes on, to satisfy the universal urge of mankind to solve the unknown. A man was once charged and fined at a magistrates' court in Britain for cutting *Times* crosswords out of issues in a public library.

Mr Wynne, we're sure, didn't guess what he was starting back in 1913. One gathers that even he wasn't especially impressed with his effort, shoved in as a filler, which was a diamond-shaped block consisting of 72 white squares around a centre of black squares. He gave readers 32 interlocking words to be guessed and the clues were straight synonyms or definitions: 'Close of day' = evening, 'Day-dream' = reverie, and so on.

The game hadn't arrived out of thin air. Wynne was working a variation on this kind of word puzzle:

```
P  H  A  S  E
H  O  V  E  L
A  V  O  I  D
S  E  I  N  E
E  L  D  E  R
```

And that had been around virtually since the birth of Christ, developing into the acrostic puzzle which gave (as Wynne did) definitions for the words. Wynne's minor revolution was the idea that the words across could be different from the words going down.

Oddly enough, considering what finally happened to the crossword, there wasn't much reaction for almost a decade. One New York *World* editor recalled: 'The puzzle obviously had a big following, but was regarded in the office as beneath a sensible man's consideration.' Maybe the First World War and its gloomy aftermath took people's minds off anything as frivolous as word puzzles. Maybe the early crosswords were too full of typographers' errors for many solvers to get the idea. Indeed, as late as 1923 *The Times* appeared not even to have heard of the latest form of word puzzle since it felt it worth while to devote an editorial called 'The Tyranny of the Acrostic' to the crossword's precursor.

The 'shop' of Acrostics is today becoming a form of conversation in which all can join. It is heard on every side ... There are also some who may be called acrostic touts. They do not compete themselves but ply the lexicon on behalf of someone else, usually a lady, who has several such guessing cavaliers in her train ... More often than not they are left protesting that the composer has cheated them by some low device, some meaning of a word perhaps only to be found in an American dictionary.

In 1924, however, the crossword really came into its own. In

Britain, the first newspaper crossword was published in the *Sunday Express*, while in America two bright young publishers named Richard Simon and Max Shuster brought out the first book of crosswords. Within a year it sold 400,000 copies at $1.35 under the imprint of the Plaza Publishing Company (because Messrs S. and S. were ashamed, at first, for it to be known as *their* book?) and, with sales of dictionaries and *Roget's Thesaurus* also rocketing, the fad was established.

Most newspapers began to publish daily crosswords. In America there were crossword tournaments galore – Yale against Harvard, Brooklyn against Manhattan, cops versus firemen – while a Chicago wife was given a divorce on the grounds that she had become a 'crossword widow'. In London, pickpockets were reportedly doing good business either by helping solvers in hotel lobbies or by pretending to be solvers themselves and seeking the assistance of prospective victims. And the New York *World*, which had started it all, got a poet (Gelett Burgess) to compile a crossword for them, announcing it aptly:

> The fans they chew their pencils,
> The fans they beat their wives
> They look up words for extinct birds –
> They live such puzzling lives.

Yet the crossword, hailed in America as 'the greatest known foe of boredom', was to become rather a bore itself once the composers began to run out of obvious words. During the mid-1920s, crosswords became bogged down with a sticky mass of exotic and unfamiliar words, so much so that in America the *Bookman* magazine could publish a long dialogue between two women which went in part like this:

MRS W.: What is that you're working at, my dear?

MRS F.: I'm tatting Joe's initials on his moreen vest. Are you making that ebon garment for yourself?

MRS W.: Yea. Just a black dress for everyday. Henry says I look rather naïf in black.

MRS F.: Well, perhaps; but it's a bit too anile for me. Give me something in indigo, or, say, ecru.

MRS W.: Quite right. There is really no neb in such solemn vestments.

MRS F.: Stet.

MRS W.: By the way, didn't I hear that your little Junior met with an accident?

9

MRS F.: Yes. The little oaf fell from an apse and fractured his artus.
MRS W.: Egad!

Not, in truth, that the fashion for such cliché crossword phrases has ever died out entirely. In 1959, under the heading 'Crossword Country', the letters page of *The Times* had a running correspondence about the subject. A reader in Paris wrote:

Sir – I have amused myself recently by visualising 'Crossword Country'. It consists largely of tors covered with heather (ling) and the predominating fauna are ernes, hens, lions, asps and she-cats. They feed, as appropriate, on grubs, sole, bass, ants, bees and each other. There are, unfortunately, also humans, all dastards, renegades or rips, except for some dons, doctors, Royal Engineers and tars (A.B.s). Their names are Mac, Ian, or Eli. This regrettable population is kept going with the collaboration of lasses or maids named Eve and Vera who, necessarily, become Ma, as Mac and Co. become Pa.

To which another correspondent, among many, added:

Three birds should, I think, be added to the fauna: the emu, dodo and kiwi. Mammals very much in evidence include agouta, agouti, coati, koala, okapi and panda. As for humans, there is a handsome gaggle of girls: Mimi, Fifi, Gigi, Bebe, Hebe, Hera, Hero and Dido. Their boyfriends cannot all be enumerated. Some have names of Biblical provenance: Elihu, Agag, Noah, and his sons, Beeri and Sisera. Others frequently encountered include Plato, Cato, Tito, Omar, Odo, Koko, Casca, Cicero. Bob and Penny (referred to by their initials) become increasingly active: should Bob ail, we are about to leave port; but should Penny ail, we are legislating for Eire.*

It was clear that the crossword had to get out of the rut of rocs, emus, apods and apses into which it had slipped. And, jointly, it was probably the *New York Times* and *The Times* of London which did the most to widen the scope of the puzzle. The New York paper was the leader with innovations such as phrases instead of single words in the grids, quotations with missing words, and the use of proper names and topical references. 'Having your name appear in the Sunday crossword is like getting free room and board in the Hall of Fame for a week,' a celebrity once observed. And once *The Times* added its thunder, the pace quickened still more.

* 'Bob ail' = S ('s was the abbreviation for 'shilling' or 'bob') + AIL = SAIL (about to leave port). 'Penny ail' = D (former abbreviation for 'penny') + AIL = DAIL (Irish legislative assembly).

The first daily crossword appeared in *The Times* on 1 February 1930, in response to a suggestion in a letter from one Lieutenant-Commander A. C. Powell. It had a rough ride early on – 'pandering to the modern craze for passing the time in all sorts of stupid ways', one correspondent among scores of angry readers bewailed – and it took a veteran American solver over an hour and half to finish. So livid were the complaints that Auntie *Times* was compromising her dignity, that crosswords in Latin and Greek were swiftly published in an attempt to gain respectability. Then came the development of ever more involved puzzles with anagrams, sometimes avowed, sometimes cunningly disguised; ghastly puns; inversions; subtle divisions of words and phrases to suggest meanings different from their surface interpretation; bizarre allusions to history, geography, literature, music, sports and games. The crossword audience of *The Times* was seen as an 'eclectic, versatile, whimsical, cultivated fellowship – an audience of intellectual magpies', grappling with the compiler in 'an ever-renewed but always good-tempered battle of wits, in which the last thing that anyone wants is a final victory for either side'. The compiler himself was imagined to be 'a canon of Barchester and a member of the Pickwick Club [who] attends concerts of classical music only but keeps in touch with the frivolities of the contemporary stage, regrets the advance of mechanisation but consoles himself by growing rare blooms for the Royal Horticultural Society's shows'. He was actually several people, but most notably Mr Adrian Bell, who composed Crossword No. 1, wore out a dictionary a year, and whose fiancée was congratulated by her prospective father-in-law thus: 'You have the sort of mind which will help Adrian with his crosswords.'

In those early days there were constant outbreaks of letters to *The Times* from crossword fans, who included Ian Hay, Sir Max Beerbohm, John Masefield, P. G. Wodehouse and the Archbishop of York. Among the most interesting was one (August 1934) which went:

I want to claim a record. A few weeks ago, when no policeman was looking, a bookstall keeper in Berlin boldly sold me a copy of *The Times*. I started the crossword as the train left and finished it 40 hours later, when I arrived at Moscow. Can anyone beat this? Time must be taken off for such sleep as can be got on a train and a considerable time spent in convincing officials on the Russian frontier that I had no firearms concealed on my person. Sir Austen Chamberlain claims that the Provost of Eton polishes off these puzzles while his breakfast egg is boiling. If it boiled while he did this one. I say without hesitation that, while the school may have been Eton, I am quite sure the egg wasn't.

The crossword was, at the same time, being hailed as having made travel so much more interesting, revolutionised the life of the Stock Exchange and eliminated the silence barriers between permanent residents in hotels. By September 1938, when Chamberlain was heralding the false dawn of Munich, *The Times* could write an ingenuous editorial which began: 'Who would have thought 15 years ago that the crossword puzzle had come to stay? To most of us then it looked like a transatlantic craze which could not be expected to take root in solid, unimaginative British minds.' Later, in May 1944, before the Anglo-American invasion of northern Europe had taken place, *The Times* was still at it. 'The sight of our fellow travellers in a suburban railway carriage, each with contracted brow and tapping pencil attacking his daily crossword, makes us wonder whether as a race we are growing more intellectual.'

We don't really swallow that, but certainly the development of crosswords since the Second World War has tended increasingly to make the clues themselves more baffling rather than the answers. Obscure words as answers seem to us to be the desperate last resort of a composer. In over 30 years of puzzle compiling, including 20 for the *Sunday Times* (which has run puzzles since the 1920s), we had not always been above doing that ourselves, but we regarded the need to put in bizarre answers as a defeat. The compiler's job, we think, should be to wrap up reasonably ordinary words in clues which are ultimately seen to be fair by the solver, but which, until the moment of breakthrough, disguise the answer in the wittiest possible way. Word play is the summit of crossword achievement and clues should encourage the imagination of the solver to expand, to freewheel through all kinds of word-and-idea associations. The sort of clues we most enjoy are the cryptics. Such clues have a huge range, which we shall be explaining later, but a few examples will give the idea. The answer to the clue 'Rough's companion' is 'Ready'; 'Evergreen creeper' leads to 'Grass snake' (isn't that beautifully succinct and precise?); and 'It is topping to kiss a monkey' works out as 'Apex' ('Ape' + 'X').

British puzzles at their best tend to be the most avant-garde in the world. Yet even the most daunting clues should be understandable once the ground rules of the game are known – even that clue from *The Times* which read 'Anne of Cleves cried "No"!', to which the answer was 'Neighed'. The solver here is required to have cognisance of the fact that Anne of Cleves was known as the 'Flanders Mare'! When *The Times* holds its regular National Crossword Contest it does indeed strain the quick-wittedness and breadth of knowledge of those who enter. Many thousands of readers enter this competition each year. In 1970, for example, there were 20,000 entrants and, of the 2,000 who were left by the time of the final elimination puzzle, half were knocked out by a clue which called for knowledge of the word 'uffish', which is contained in the invented vocabulary of Lewis Carroll's poem 'Jabberwocky', from *Through the Looking Glass* (the poem that begins ''Twas brillig, and the slithy toves did gyre and gimble in the wabe'). Most of them wrote 'uppish' as the answer. There was another clue which gave trouble. It read, 'They hang from trees in the Book of Jeremiah', to which the answer was 'Amenta' (catkins). Perhaps the compiler may also sadistically have imagined frantic competitors scouring the Book of Jeremiah to find the answer, when there it was all the time, staring them in the face as a 'contained word' in the very title of the book, which correctly reads: '**lamenta**tions of Jeremiah'. It may be a humbling thought that the record time for completing the *Times* crossword under test conditions was 3 minutes 45 seconds by a civil servant named Roy Dean from Bromley, Kent, on 19 December 1970, in a BBC studio during the course of a programme called 'Today'!

There is nothing as devilish as that 'Jeremiah' clue or 'uffish' in the puzzles in this book, but to solve them you need to know something about the conventions of cryptic crosswords. If you're already an experienced solver, you may (except out of curiosity) stop reading now. But if you're a (relative) newcomer, an explanation of the more important ground rules may help.

2 HOW TO SOLVE CRYPTIC CROSSWORDS

Word play is the essence of cryptic crosswords. It can appear in many forms in the clues, but the chief kinds are these:

a Word divisions
b Liberties with punctuation, etc.
c Inversions of words or parts of words; leaving out bits of words, etc.
d Anagrams
e 'Contained-word' or hidden clues
f 'Sound-word' clues
g Use of abbreviations
h Disguise of verbs as nouns, nouns as verbs, etc.
i Puns and double meanings
j Overt or disguised references to literature, etc.
k Special crossword conventions
l Quotations

We'll lead you through examples of each of these before arriving at a complete specimen of a cryptic crossword with an explanation of each answer. Some of the examples given – though by no means all – are taken from puzzles in this series.

a Word divisions

Many words given as answers in crosswords split into two or more words which have meaning in themselves. Take the word 'redstart', which is a kind of bird. It breaks into 'red' + 'start', and a simple cryptic clue for this could be 'Revolutionary innovation by a bird'. The clue indicates 'red' by the straight synonym 'revolutionary', and 'start' by another straight synonym, 'innovation'; it also indicates the meaning of the whole answer by telling you it's 'a bird'. This is the most straightforward way of clueing an answer on the principle of word division.

Sometimes words (e.g. 'added to', 'receiving', etc.) will be put into the clue indicating that parts of the answer, 'join up' to form the whole. An example would be:

'The embassy *receives* a sign from heaven: must be religious types! (12)'

    Answer: MISSIONARIES – in which MISSION is 'the embassy', plus ARIES as 'a sign from heaven', ending up as MISSIONARIES, who are 'religious types'.

An answer may also be broken up into two or more words, however, in a different way. Take the word 'defenders'. This can be broken up thus: DEF(END)ERS, i.e. the word END is included in the word DEFERS. A clue for this would, quite fairly, read: 'They don't attack delays without consequence (9)'. The answer DEFENDERS is defined by 'They don't attack'; DEFERS is defined by its synonym 'delays' (which misleads you in the clue because you should read it as a *verb*, but it looks as if it's a noun); and DEFERS is stated to be 'without' (i.e. 'outside', though, again, this isn't the obvious way to read it) the word END, given in the clue as its synonym 'consequence'.

This kind of word-division clue is frequently signalled by the use of certain give-away words in clues. Apart from the cunning 'without', other such phrases are 'outside', 'inside', 'among', 'holding', 'surrounding', 'interrupting'. Here are examples of these – and at this point we're going to start using a shorthand form of explanation which shows how the answers are broken up in the clue. The italicized words would not normally be italicized, but are here put in this form to emphasize the 'instruction' words(s) in the clues:

'French nobleman *among* the offspring led astray (7)'

    Answer: SEDUCED – SE(DUC)ED.

'Attack the stupid creature who's *holding* one back (8)'

    Answer: DENOUNCE – D(ENO)UNCE (NB 'one back' = 'one reversed').

'Was still adopting an assumed attitude in revolutionary *surroundings* (7)'

    Answer: REPOSED – RE(POSE)D (NB 'reposed' means 'was still').

'Famous naturalist and doctor interrupted by a triumph (6)'

    Answer: DARWIN – D(A)R/WIN (DR – 'doctor' – interrupted by 'A', plus WIN – 'triumph').

b Liberties with punctuation, etc.

You've already noticed, no doubt, that in some of the sample clues given above, part of the mystification is caused by omission of punctuation which, were it there, would help the solver a great deal to read the clue as it *should* be read in order to arrive at the answer. Had there been a full stop or semicolon or dash after 'Was still' it would have made the solving easier, but the fun less. You'll find many examples of liberties with punctuation in cryptic crosswords. It's part of the game. Never accept at face value the way a clue *appears* to read. Look at these samples:

'A heavyweight goes to Alabama for an unusual kind of music (6)'

Answer: ATONAL – A/TON/AL. We all know that a TON is a 'heavy weight'; but when the two words are run together, the image is of a boxer rather than anything else – and it's meant to mislead. AL is used as an abbreviation for 'Alabama'.

'Tom following Diana – indeed devoted! (9)'

Answer: DEDICATED – DE(DICAT)ED. A tricky clue, but one which reveals a very common crossword convention. 'Diana' is DI; she's followed by CAT ('TOM'); and the whole lot is *'in* DEED', but those two words have been run together to make 'indeed' with the intention of defying the solver. But you won't let compilers frustrate you for long if you remember that nine times out of ten (well, maybe eight), the word 'indeed' in a clue signifies that you're trying to wrap 'de—ed' around something else. (Cf. also the word 'inside', which often needs to be read 'in side'.)

c Inversions of words or parts of words; leaving out bits of words, etc.

Once you've discovered that answers can be broken up into separate parts, be prepared also for the way in which compilers will signal to you that those parts have got to be treated in particular ways. Here's an example:

'I'm reversing to run at top speed, or is that literally wrong? (8)'

Answer: MISPRINT – MI/SPRINT. The phrase 'I'm' in the clue is reversed to make 'MI'; 'to run at top speed' is a definition of SPRINT; and MISPRINT is defined (with a touch of pun) in the clue as something that's 'literally wrong'. So watch out in clues for words like 'overturned', 'upset', 'return', 'going back', 'set back', 'climbing' (in down clues) as well as 'reverse', all of which indicate that a part of the answer (or the whole answer) contains a part of the clue (or its synonym) *reversed*.

A still further variation of these tricks is that the clue will indicate that the answer contains only *part* of what the clue is giving you. A few examples are better than generalised explanations to give you the idea.

'Opening your mouth and losing your head in the shelter (6)'

Answer: AWNING – (Y)AWNING. 'Opening your mouth' would be 'yawning'. It loses its 'head' (i.e. its first letter) to become AWNING, a 'shelter'.

'He lost his head, then ran with long strides and escaped with the girl! (6)'

Answer: ELOPED – (H)/LOPED. 'He lost his head' indicates the letter E; 'ran with long strides' defines LOPED; and 'escaped with the girl' indicates the answer, ELOPED.

'Speaking acidly, as it were, when giving can back to unvigorous Richard (6)'

Answer: NITRIC – NIT/RIC(HARD). 'Can back' in the clue indicates 'tin' reversed to give NIT; 'unvigorous Richard' means that the part of 'Richard' meaning 'vigorous' ('hard') is omitted to give RIC; 'Speaking acidly' points to the answer, NITRIC.

'Apportions great quantities to Alabama first (6)'

Answer: ALLOTS – AL/LOTS. 'Great quantities' in the clue signifies LOTS in the answer: 'Alabama' points to AL, an abbreviation for 'Alabama', and 'first' indicates that you've to put AL before LOTS; 'apportions' in the clue is the meaning of the whole answer, ALLOTS.

To indicate *all* the warning signs in clues which will tell you that bits of words or whole words are to be moved around would be impossible, but as soon as you see expressions like 'un-', 'headless', 'beheaded', 'doesn't start', 'doesn't begin', then beware. Note, too, that the phrases 'I leave' or 'I omitted' will often mean that the letter 'i' is going to be dropped out of a word (or synonym) in the clue in order to build up the answer (e.g., 'I leave the point with nothing on to reach part of the bridge' would give the answer PONTOON – PO(I)NT/O/ON) and that the word 'pointless' will similarly indicate that one of the letters 'N', 'W', 'E' or 'S' (the points of the compass) is going to be dropped out of the build-up given in the clue. One favourite convention is also worth a note. The clue 'Everyone in bed is hauled ashore' would obviously give the answer BEACHED – B(EACH)ED; but the compiler could easily take the clue a stage further and make it read, 'Everyone *between sheets* is hauled ashore' (which would be still more baffling since 'sheets' means 'ropes' on a boat).

d   Anagrams

An anagram is a word or phrase formed by rearranging the letters of another word or phrase. In the old crossword days, anagrams were labelled clearly as such; so a clue might read simply, 'Caned (anag.)'. Answer DANCE. But today, anagrams are indicated much more subtly. Any word in a clue which can possibly mean, either literally or figuratively, that the order of the letters in other words in the clue is to be changed may give you the tip that you've got an anagram on your hands. Let's start by giving you a few examples. In the simplest anagram one word (or several words in succession) is (are) the one(s) from which you're going to make up the answer. Like this:

'When *a male is* mangled no wonder you have a feeling of sickness! (7)'

> *Answer:* MALAISE. You've been told to 'mangle' ('mutilate') the phrase 'a male is' – rather appropriately in view of the answer.

The next stage of an anagram is when the words you're looking for are *not* consecutive, but are linked by other words – most simply by the link words 'and' or 'with', as in this clue:

'Bit of the plumbing that gives both *pride* and *pain* (9)'

> *Answer:* DRAINPIPE. Out of which you can get (or be 'given') the two words 'pride' and 'pain'.

Thirdly, a clue may be a *part* anagram, as in this one:

'Ride at medium pace and forget the *least* variety of Eng. Lit.! (10, 5)'

> *Answer: CANTERBURY TALES – CANTER/BURY TALES. In this clue 'Ride at medium pace' = CANTER; 'forget' = BURY; whilst TALES is a 'variety' of 'least' in the clue.*

Fourthly, anagrams may be accompanied by instructions to remove letters from the anagram words or to substitute other letters (a similar convention to that under heading c). Here are three examples:

'*A pound* perhaps with *a* substitute for *love* from Italy (6)'

> *Answer:* PADUAN. The anagram words are 'a pound', indicated by 'perhaps' – but you've been instructed to substitute 'a' for 'o' ('O' = 'love' in tennis scoring), and if you do you'll find that 'a paund' will make PADUAN (someone 'from Italy').

'Disorder makes one *sell out* – and *left* out too! (6)'

> *Answer:* TOUSLE. The word TOUSLE ('Disorder' in the clue) will 'make one' the words 'sell out', except that one 'I' must disappear, which is indicated by the phrase 'left out' ('I' being the recognised abbreviation for 'left').

'Pillar constructed to order with endlessly varied skill (7)'

> *Answer:* OBELISK – O.B.E./LISK. Here, the answer is described

by 'Pillar' in the clue; you 'construct' it by placing an 'order' (O.B.E., Officer of the Order of the British Empire) with 'endlessly varied skill', which signifies 'skil' ('skill' without its final 'l', i.e. 'endlessly') with its order varied to give LISK.

Fifthly, anagrams or part-anagrams may be made even more difficult when the clue gives, instead of the word(s) of the anagram itself, *synonyms* for those words. Like this:

'But is it material to prohibit a strange, *intense dislike*? (8)'

> *Answer:* BARATHEA – BAR/A/THEA. Here the whole answer is the 'material' in the clue. It's built up thus: BAR ('prohibit') + A + THEA ('intense dislike' in the clue = 'hate', and that's the word which when written out in 'strange' fashion can become THEA).

Finally, we think that the very best kind of anagram clue is that where the *same words* combine the anagram itself *and* the instructions indicating that the clue is an anagram – as in this example:

'Spread with *speed, sir* (8)'

> *Answer:* DISPERSE. Which means 'spread' and that same 'spread' roughly indicates that you've to spread around the letters of 'speed, sir' to get the answer.

You'll already have seen a few of the phrases in the clues above which indicate that an anagram is present – 'mangled', 'gives', 'variety', 'perhaps', 'makes one', 'spread'. There are, literally, hundreds of such words and we couldn't possibly give them all. But to give you fair warning about anagrams, we went through the crosswords in one *Sunday Times* book to discover just how many different anagram 'signals' we could find. The following list has got most of those 'anagram-signal' expressions in it – in alphabetical order too. But there are doubtless many more.

all over the place
altered
another shape
anyhow, anyway
arranged, arrangement

bad
become, becoming

bend, bending
bizarre
break, breaking out
broken
by redefinition

change(d)
chaos
chop(ped) up
clumsy, clumsily
cocktail (very useful if you can make it 'gin cocktail' in the clue –
    and you can, often, because lots of words end in or contain
    'ing')
collapse(d)
comes to
confused, in confusion
construction, constructed
cracked up
crash(ed)
crazy, crazily
crumpled
crushed

damage(d)
different
disaster
disguise(d)
dish of
disorder(ed)
disposed, disposition
disturbed
drunk(en)
dug over

eccentric
engaged in
enough (to make)

far from smoothly

flaws, flawed
flustered
foolishly presented
for
fracas
from the

getting roughed up
given a face lift

hotchpotch

in
in a bad way
in a heap
in(to) a new dish
incorrect(ly)
in knots
into pieces
involved

kind (of)
knocked into shape

mad, madly
mangled
maybe
melting-pot
misinterpret(ed)
mixed, mixture
muddle(d)

new
new-fangled
new order

odd(ly)
off
organize(d)

out
outcome
out of order

perhaps
poor(ly)
potential(ly)

rebuilt
recipe
refined
reform(ed)
reorganized
repaired
resolved, resolution
revolution
rewritten
riot, riotous
rocky
rough(ly)
ruin(ed)
run amok
running in

scattered, scattering
scruffy
shape(d)
shuffle(d)
slips into
smashed, smash up
sort (of)
spoilt
state of disrepair
storm
strange(ly)
stumbling
swirling
switches

thicket
throw
tip out
transporting
trouble(d)
turbulent
turn out (to be)
twisting

unorthodox
unruly
unusual(ly)
unusual dose
upset

variety
variously

went to pieces
wild(ly)
wobbly
woolly

e   'Contained-word' or hidden clues

Clues sometimes give a hidden definition of the answer and also, literally, 'contain' the answer in the course of spelling out some of the words in the clue. The simplest way in which the compiler signals this is by words like 'in', 'of' or 'out of' in the clue. For example, 'Girl who goes out of Ber**lin da**ily'. Answer: LINDA; or, 'Comfort found in Chels**ea's e**legant houses'. Answer: EASE.

There are, as with anagrams, several words which can warn you of a 'contained-word', although they're certainly not as numerous as the anagram signals. They include 'form', 'part of', 'partially', 'falls into', and 'some of'. Here are some examples of 'contained-word' or 'split word' clues and answers:

'Poet falls into the la**ke at S**alerno (5)'

Answer: KEATS.

'Delay one's departure from Ber**lin, Ger**many (6)'

Answer: LINGER.

'In this particular case, it's some of the star players **at Chel**sea (7)'

Answer: SATCHEL.

Used by a tea**cher as er**uditely as possible (6)'

Answer: ERASER (note here that no definition of 'eraser' is included in the clue; one relies on the loose association of the fact that an 'eraser' is likely to be used by a teacher, to round out the clue).

f 'Sound-word' clues

Part of the word play in cryptic crosswords is based on the fact that some words *sound* like others (e.g. 'Eton' sounds like 'eaten'; 'aroma' sounds like 'a roamer'). Again, the best way is to give examples – but you can often expect a 'sound' clue if a clue contains expressions like 'one hears', 'I hear', 'apparently', 'it seems', 'it appears', 'from the sound of it', and so on. Examples are these:

'One hears it's more disgusting, bitter resentment (7)'

Answer: RANCOUR. It means 'bitter resentment'; it sounds like 'ranker' ('more disgusting').

'Trousers are a source of quarrels, it seems (8)'

Answer: BREECHES (sounds like 'breaches').

'A really red-blooded bit of light opera, one hears (9)'

Answer: RUDDIGORE (sounds like 'ruddy gore').

'Sounds as if it goes on and on at the breakfast table (6)'

Answer: CEREAL (sounds like 'serial').

'Goes over the top with old tennis stars apparently (7)'

Answer: EXCEEDS (sounds like 'ex-seeds').

'Mark it for special attention apparently, with a label (6)'

Answer: TICKET (sounds like 'tick it').

g Use of abbreviations

Cryptic crossword clues are full of words spelt out fully, but whose role in building up the answer is that of an *abbreviation* only. Sometimes the clue indicates, by the use of phrases like 'small', 'minor', 'quickly', 'little', 'briefly', 'shortly', etc., that you are meant to abbreviate the word, but this is by no means always so.

Frequently the solver has to deduce that an abbreviation is what's required in the answer or part-answer. Some examples of the use of abbreviations in clues:

'A heavyweight goes to *Alabama* for an unusual kind of music (6)'
> *Answer:* ATONAL. A/TON/AL; AL=Alabama.

'Final message, by direction, is mature (4)'
> *Answer:* RIPE.R.I.P./E; R.I.P. = requiescat in pace, rest in peace (thus, with word play, 'final message'); E = East ('direction').

'Crushed the publicity man first = that's what's offered for your consideration (10)'
> *Answer:* PROPOUNDED. P.R.O./POUNDED; P.R.O. = public relations officer ('publicity man'), which comes 'first' before POUNDED ('crushed').

Abbreviations cover many pages in standard works of reference such as *Chamber's Twentieth Century Dictionary* and the *Concise Oxford Dictionary*, but to give you pointers to the huge variety which can be used, here is a list covering the most common of them.

AB	=	able-bodied seaman ('sailor')
a/c } a.c. }	=	account
AD	=	anno domini ('our era', 'our time')
A1	=	first-class (note that in cryptic crosswords the letter 'i' and the figure '1' are usually regarded as interchangeable; thus in a clue the letter 'i' may be rendered as 'one')
Al, Ala	=	Alabama
a.m.	=	morning
Au	=	gold
BA	=	Bachelor of Arts (loosely, 'bachelor', 'degree', etc.)
BA	=	British Airways ('airline')
BOAC	=	British Overseas Airways Corporation ('airline'). Old-fashioned usage now
Br.	=	British, Britain, brother
C	=	100, Roman numeral (loosely 'many', 'a lot of'). Note also other Roman numerals like V = 5; VI = 6, half a dozen; X = 10; D = 500; M = 1000
CA	=	chartered accountant

CE	=	civil engineer, Church of England (strictly speaking, C of E)
CH	=	Companion of Honour (loosely, 'honourable companion', 'award', 'honour', etc.)
co.	=	company (loosely, 'firm', etc.)
cr.	=	credit
D/d	=	date, daughter, democrat, died, penny (as it once was – loosely, 'copper'), degree
DA	=	District Attorney (thus 'US lawyer', etc.)
DD	=	Doctor of Divinity (loosely, 'doctor')
dept.	=	department
Di	=	Diana
Dr	=	Doctor
ed.	=	editor, edition
e.g.	=	for example, for instance
enc.	=	enclosure
EP	=	extended play (loosely, 'record', 'disc')
f/ff	=	forte (loosely, 'loud', 'strong', 'very loud', etc.)
Fri.	=	Friday (cf. other days of the week – Sun., Mon., Tues., Wed., Thurs., Sat.)
Gen/gen.	=	Genesis, general(ly)
i/c, i.c.	=	in charge (of)
i.e.	=	that is
IOM	=	Isle of Man (loosely , 'Man')
IRA	=	Irish Republican Army (loosely, 'illegal army', 'illegal organization', etc.)
Kt	=	knight
L/l.	=	learner (thus, loosely, 'beginner', 'novice', 'tyro', etc.), line, lira, licentiate, left
lab.	=	laboratory (loosely, 'scientific centre', etc.)
Lab.	=	Labour (loosely, 'politician')
Lib.	=	Liberal (loosely, 'politician')
LP	=	long play(ing) (loosely, 'record', 'disc', etc.)
ma	=	mother (loosely, 'parent')
MA	=	Master of Arts (loosely, 'master', 'degree', etc.)
MB	=	Medicinae Baccalaureus – Bachelor of Medicine (loosely, 'doctor')
MO	=	Medical Officer (loosely, 'doctor')
MP	=	Member of Parliament (loosely 'politician')

OBE	=	Officer of the Order of the British Empire (loosely, 'award', 'honour', 'order')
OS	=	outsize, very large
p/pp	=	piano (loosely, 'soft', 'quiet', etc.), participle
pa/Pa	=	father (loosely, 'dad', 'parent'), Pennsylvania
pro	=	in favour of (loosely, 'a person in favour of'), professional
PRO	=	Public Relations Officer (loosely, 'publicity man', etc.)
pt	=	point
R/Rt	=	right, royal
RA	=	Royal Artillery (loosely, 'gunner(s)', 'corps', etc.), Royal Academician (loosely, 'artist', 'painter')
re	=	about, concerning, with regard to, in the case of
RE	=	Royal Engineers (loosely, 'sapper(s)', 'engineer(s)', 'corps', etc.)
RI	=	Rhode Island
RMS	=	Royal Mail Ship (loosely, 'ship', 'liner', 'mailboat', etc.)
RN	=	Royal Navy (loosely, 'navy', 'fleet', 'sailors', etc.)
RU	=	Rugby Union (i.e. Rugby football)
ry/rly	=	railway
S/s	=	second(s), shilling (former coin – hence, loosely, 'Bob', 'old Bob'), sister
SA	=	South Africa
Sal	=	Sarah
sis	=	sister
sop.	=	soprano
sp.	=	specialist
SP	=	starting-price (i.e. of a horse in a horse-race; loosely, 'final odds')
SS	=	steamship (loosely, 'ship', 'liner')
St/st	=	saint (loosely, 'holy man', etc.), street (loosely 'highway', 'way', etc.)
tr.	=	translator, translation
U	=	upper class (loosely, 'socially acceptable'; cf. non-U)

UN	=	United Nations (loosely, 'international organis-ation', 'international government', etc.)
US USA	=	United States of America
Va	=	Virginia

h Disguise of verbs as nouns, nouns as verbs, etc.

Clues will also try to make the solver believe that a particular part of speech should be read as a different part of speech. No rules can be made to cover this, but a few examples will illustrate what you face:

'Want hatred to crumble (6)'

> *Answer:* DEARTH. 'Hatred' in the clue is its anagram (indicated by 'crumble') and its meaning is 'want' (noun) whereas the clue suggests it should be read as a verb.

'The most sensible like returning home (6)'

> *Answer:* SANEST – SA/NEST. Here 'like' suggests itself as a verb, but it isn't; it's an informal preposition, roughly equivalent to 'as' which you've to reverse ('like returning') to build up SA, the first part of the answer.

'Quiet husband left inside (5)'

> *Answer:* SALVE – SA(L)VE. A real brute! 'Quiet' is a verb meaning 'to salve'; 'husband' is a verb too, meaning SAVE; 'inside' the word SAVE, place L (= 'left', abbreviation) and you get SALVE.

i Puns and double meanings

Again, you can't make rules about this, but since puns and double meanings are the heart and soul of cryptic crosswords, an explanation of some examples will serve as a guide:

'House a poet whilst making spanners (8,7)'

> *Answer:* BUILDING BRIDGES. A BUILDING could be a 'house'; BRIDGES is a 'poet' (Robert Bridges); and if you're BUILDING BRIDGES you're 'making spanners' (i.e. objects that span).

'Performed by many willing people? (8)'

> *Answer:* EXECUTED. People who carry out wills (i.e. 'willing people') are 'executing' wills.

'Heated singer! (6)'

Answer: KETTLE. Kettles 'sing' as they approach boiling point.

'Beloved and belobed? (8)'

> *Answer:* ENDEARED – END/EARED. A gentle play on words since the 'lobes' are at the 'end' of the 'ears', so a coining is invented for the clue, 'belobed'

'Could easily be standing in the view of others (8)'

> *Answer:* PRESTIGE.

j   Overt or disguised references to literature, etc.

A couple of examples:

'Land of Hope (9)'

> *Answer:* RURITANIA. Remember 'Land of Hope and Glory, Mother of the Free'? Well, this has nothing to do with it – though the compiler hopes the solver will think it has! It's a reference to the novel *Prisoner of Zenda* by Anthony Hope, whose setting was the imaginary kingdom of Ruritania in Central Europe.

'Haggard heroine gets the record for mutton! (5)'

> *Answer:* SHEEP – SHE/E.P. No, the heroine isn't haggard. The reference is to Rider Haggard's novel *She*. The 'record' is an E.P. (extended play).

k   Special crossword conventions

You will have realised from the letters on 'Crossword Country' in *The Times* quoted on page 10 that cryptic crosswords have attracted to themselves a host of traditions and conventions. When a clue mentions the word 'degree', it's almost certain to be the letters 'MA' or 'BA' you're going to put in the answer somewhere. If it's a 'politician', you're looking for 'MP', or 'Lib', 'Lab', 'Soc' or 'Tory'. When 'parson' or 'minister' crops up, expect 'Rev'. The word 'gallery' should usually point you to 'Tate'. And you're going to turn 'the French' into 'le', 'la' or 'les'; 'the little devil' into 'imp'; 'love' into 'o' (that's tennis); and 'a beautiful young man' into 'Apollo'.

There are rather more subtle conventions which should be mentioned. The initials 'SS' stand for 'steamship', 'liner'. So a word like 'shops' might be clued, 'Jump in a ship to get stores' – S(HOP)S. Loosening up the clue further, it could read 'Jump on board to get stores'. When you see 'on board' in a clue it's an almost certain sign that the letters 'S—S' will be wrapped around something. Another convention is the use of the word 'initially', as in this clue: 'Old boy initially has a valet carefully attentive', to which the answer is OBSERVANT (O.B./SERVANT). 'Initially' indicates that you want the initial letters of 'old boy' as part of the solution.

Another convention. Come across the phrase 'with some hesitation' or 'hesitantly' or 'sound of hesitation' in a clue and the chances are that the letters 'er' or 'um' will be needed as a section of the answer. For instance:

'Second sound of hesitation creates the impetus (8)'

> *Answer:* MOMENTUM – MOMENT/UM. 'Second' = MOMENT; 'sound of hesitation' = UM.

'Without hesitation suffer anger in the vote (8)'

> *Answer:* SUFFRAGE – SUFF(ER)/RAGE. In this clue you've to *remove* the sound of hesitation (ER), as indicated by '*without* hesitation', from the clue word 'suffer'. That gives you SUFF to which you add RAGE ('anger').

To explain such conventions doesn't mean that crossword clues depend entirely on them by any means, nor that crosswords are full of clichés. But it's as well to know a few of the more common tricks of the trade. Here's a quick guide to some of them, with the likely word in the clue given *first*, and how it should be interpreted given on the right-hand side of the equation. The list includes some simple foreign words too:

a French	= un, une
after the pattern of	= in
all right	= OK
alternative, alternative word	= or
ancient city	= Ur (Ur of the Chaldees)
at home	= in
away, not at home	= out
banker	= river (i.e., something with banks)
bloomer	= flower (i.e., something that blooms; useful because 'bloomer' is slang for 'blunder')

by way of	= in
circle	= O
Communist	= Red
correct	= OK
dear French	= cher
direction	= N, S, E, or W
Edward (little Edward)	= Ted
first-class	= ai (AI)
flower	= river (i.e., something that flows!)
former	= ex
from foreign ⎫ from French ⎭	= de
Henry (little Henry)	= Hal
in the fashion of ⎫ in the style of ⎭	= à la
in the main	= in the sea
Irishman	= Pat
is French	= est
Jack	= knave (cards), sailor
key	= A, B, C, D, E, F, or G
kiss	= X
late	= ex
let it be, let it stand, don't change it, etc.	= stet
little way	= rd (road), st (street)
London district	= EC, WC, SW, etc.
love	= O
Mediterranean	= Med.
Muse	= Erato (usually!)
note	= A, B, C, D, E, F, or G
of foreign ⎫ of French ⎭	= de
of the French	= du, des
one	= i
one-time	= ex
piper's son	= Tom
quarter	= SW, NW, NE, SE, etc.
revolutionary	= red
Richard (little Richard)	= Dick

ring	= O
same	= idem, id.
said in France says in France	= dit
Scotsman	= Ian
spot marker	= X (viz.: 'X marks the spot')
tea, tee	= T
the first letter	= alpha
the French	= le, la les
the French dance	= bal
the French sea the sea abroad	= mer
the Italian	= il
the last letter	= omega
the last word	= amen
the Spanish	= el
30-second	= min. (i.e., half a *min*ute; confusing since 'min' can also represent 'minute', being the official abbreviation for the word)
this French	= ce
Tom	= cat
unknown quantity	= X
very French	= très
wall abroad	= mur
was in the van	= led
way (e.g. 'in a way')	= rd (road), st (street)
who in France	= qui
writer	= pen
yes abroad yes in Germany	= ja

1 Quotations

In these, you simply have to fill in the missing word, which is indicated by a space left in the clue – thus:

'The quality of—is not strain'd, (*The Merchant of Venice*) (5)

   Answer: MERCY

3 SPECIMEN PUZZLE

And finally, to give beginners, or relative beginners, a clear idea of how one particular puzzle is solved, here is a sample crossword, filled in as it would be on completion, with the clues and explanations of those clues. The number of letters in the answer is given in parentheses at the end of each clue.

ACROSS

1 Cooler on the road, but warmer in the house (8)
5 Spanish fish seen in clouds of flying water (6)
9 How to carry baby – or is that revolting? (2, 2, 4)
10 Water-spirit in nude perhaps (6)
12 He's not treated in an honourable way! (6)
13 Was destroyed by means of one storage structure (8)
15 Grassy area on which a sporting gesture is made with bias! (7-5)
18 For each exciting experience in ancient times, perhaps (12)
23 They cut off ships (8)
24 All-rounder turning over an afterthought in this place? (6)
26 Maybe the singer is boss (6)
27 Town that certainly *ought* to be shown on a relief map (8)
28 Importance of acquiring some piastres suddenly (6)
29 Expedients in poetic metres? (8)

DOWN

1 Manhandles hoodlums (6)
2 Condescends to change the design (6)
3 A girl I love beside the seaside abroad! (7)
4 Resistance units working for the Queen ... (4)
6 ... using sharp steel against her husband in the act of stabbing! (7)
7 Didn't stay on to arrange a deal about some kind of pointless thing (8)
8 Series not yet decided? Exhausting, isn't it? (8)
11 Sent up a mixed bag of monkey food (7)

14 Symbolically calculating approach to problems (7)
16 Naturally they'll go for pure ices, won't they? (8)
17 Almost entirely princely, and altogether more clever (8)
19 Relies for support in trusts (7)
20 About to squeeze and put down (7)
21 One who refuses to admit the fineness of the stocking? (6)
22 Inclines to being Dogberry's partner? (6)
25 Mincemeat is so uninspiring (4)

34

NOTES ON THE ANSWERS

ACROSS

1 RADIATOR is a play on words; a 'radiator' is a 'warmer' (i.e. a heater) in the home, but in a vehicle (indicated by 'on the road' in the clue) it's a cooling agent (i.e. a 'cooler')

5 SPRAYS: the meaning of the whole is 'clouds of flying water'; you build it up via SP (= 'Spanish', abbreviation) + RAYS (= 'fish')

9 UP IN ARMS means 'revolting' (i.e. in a state of revolt). The phrase can also loosely signify 'how to carry baby' – a clue involving word play.

10 UNDINE, a 'water-spirit'; anagram, 'in nude', indicated by 'perhaps'

12 HONEST means 'honourable'; anagram, 'he's not', indicated by 'treated (in an honourable way)'

13 PERISHED means 'was destroyed'; built up by PER (= 'by means of') + I (= 'one') + SHED (= 'storage structure')

15 BOWLING-GREEN is a play on words; BOWLING-GREEN is the 'grassy area'; the bowls used are weighted so that they roll with a bias (which can also mean 'prejudice', and that forms the basis of the word play)

18 PERADVENTURE means 'perhaps', archaic – and, hence, the clue says 'in ancient times'. Built up with PER (= 'for each' + ADVENTURE (= 'exciting experience')

23 CLIPPERS means both 'ships' and 'cutting instrument', hence 'they cut off' in the clue, a play on words

24 SPHERE is indicated in the clue by 'all-rounder' (word play for a 'round' or 'globular' object). Built up by SP (= PS reversed, i.e. 'turning over' PS; PS means ('post=scriptum' or, as the clue has it, 'afterthought', a slight word play) + HERE (= 'in this place')

26 REIGNS means 'is boss' (i.e. is predominant, has power); anagram, 'singer', indicated by 'maybe'

27 MAFEKING: word play on Mafeking, the South African town, the relief of which was so notable an incident in the Boer War

28 STRESS is a 'contained-word' clue. STRESS = 'import-ance', and to get the answer you have to 'acquire a certain amount of' the phrase 'pia**stres** suddenly'

29 MEASURES means both 'expedients' and 'poetic metres', a simple example of a double-meaning or double-synonym clue

DOWN

1 ROUGHS means both 'manhandles' and 'hoodlums', another double-meaning clue

2 DEIGNS means 'condescends'; anagram, 'design', as indic-ated by 'to change'

3 ALASSIO is an Italian seaside resort, hence, 'beside the seaside abroad'. The build-up is A LASS (= 'a girl') + I (= 'I') + O (= 'love', the famous tennis parallel, in which 'love' means 'zero', '0' in scoring)

4 OHMS is given as 'resistance units' in the clue, which begins the word play (OHM is 'a unit of electrical resistance'). OHMS is also, of course, the abbreviation for On Her Majesty's Service (i.e. 'working for the Queen'). This clue is allowed to run on (...) simply because it links neatly with the next clue, a common cryptic crossword convention

6 PINKLING means 'the act of stabbing'. Built up with PIN (= 'sharp steel') + (i.e. 'against') KING (= 'her husband', meaning the queen's husband)

7 ALIGHTED – the clue indicates this by 'didn't stay on' (i.e. got off). The build-up is AL(IGHT)ED – anagram, 'deal', indicated by 'to arrange', which is placed 'about' anagram, 'thing', indicated by 'some kind of', minus the letter 'n' (point of the compass – hence 'pointless thing' in the clue)

8 SPENDING is given as 'exhausting' in the clue; built up by S (= abbreviation for 'series') + PENDING (= 'not yet decided')

11 PEANUTS is 'monkey food' in the clue; anagram, 'sent up a', indicated aptly by 'mixed bag of'

14 ALGEBRA is a play on words; algebra uses symbols to work out arithmetical (hence, association with 'calculating') prob-lems

16 EPICURES is an anagram, 'pure ices', indicated by 'go for';

the clue not requiring a strict definition of 'epicures', since such people would certainly only go for *pure* ices

17 BRAINIER means 'more clever'; built up by (B)RAINIER (i.e. Prince Rainier, hence, 'princely', Rainier forming 'almost entirely' the word required)

19 DEPENDS is a double-meaning clue; answer means 'relies for support' and 'trusts' (verb)

20 REPRESS means (to) 'put-down'; constructed with RE (= 'about', i.e. regarding, concerning) + (indicated by 'to', i.e. joined to) PRESS (= 'squeeze')

21 DENIER is a word play with a double meaning: 'one who refuses to admit' and 'fineness of stocking'

22 VERGES means 'inclines (to)'; Verges was Dogberry's partner (a fellow town-constable) in Shakespeare's *Much Ado About Nothing*

25 TAME means 'uninspiring' (i.e. insipid, lacking interest); anagram, 'meat', as aptly indicated by 'mincemeat'

ELIZABETH AND DEREK JEWELL

I

ACROSS

1 Ought the monarch to jostle so? (8)
5 Top man in his trade is to point afterwards (6)
9 Minutely reviewed as inappropriate to the occasion (8)
10 Make mummy bring me back some ointment (6)
12 Quick job for the vicar (6)
13 Put off from holding a tin – a bottle is needed (8)
15 Polish workers increase production (7)
16 Tea perhaps, in the garden (4)
20 An act with a twist to it (4)
21 Unrelenting, like a fox circling a bird (7)
25 Fellows curse at what they have to don (8)
26 Present odds on the field (6)
28 Spotted, and because of this I went in van (6)
29 Guile tar deployed, tying up (8)
30 Father after parking tries to move (6)
31 Lots delivered by the cat (8)

DOWN

1 Sudden blow and scream (6)
2 Notes of a month on the road (6)
3 Sorry because the chaps are coming in afterwards? (8)
4 Some feel slippery (4)
6 Left Burma, travelling to nether regions (6)
7 Drawing for the pamphlet I take on (8)
8 Commented on a sign in the grass (8)
11 Forms new partnership and goes off (7)
14 Butt in here? (7)
17 Pays at the end of the test match (6,2)
18 Drinking songs Italian port inspired (8)
19 Friends turn up then hurry off in a casual way (8)
22 We set about starters first, then have these? (6)
23 Work lathe again to make a profit (6)
24 Though not a form of currency they have purchasing power (6)
27 Edge on which you'll find a crack (4)

2

ACROSS

1 Can train team once left floundering (5,9)
10 Pensioners got up, seeking shade (3,4)
11 Rig cast adrift, affecting stomach (7)
12 The racing game (9)
13 Fruit softly rounded (5)
14 Pest with a hairy tail? (6)
15 It perches outside on treetop in the most elegant way (8)
18 Showing even less enthusiasm about the article – it won't hold water (8)
20 Free-for-all, wearing bloomers (6)
23 A ship swallowed by the deep (5)
25 Sudden victory perhaps, after hovering around? Precisely! (9)
26 Draws around – tucks in (7)
27 Form of postage once in force in Germany (7)
28 Ton-up drug dealers? (5,9)

DOWN

2 Wonder about entertaining everyone, being the one providing support (7)
3 Declaring love for a girl? Not I, perversely (9)
4 Controls foreign nationals, we hear (6)
5 Absence of something, for example, in the community (8)
6 Author sending up pea-jacket for only son (5)
7 Tend to run true to form (7)
8 Summing up, I turn to a place I recollect (14)
9 Takes retaliatory action when adder attacks? (7-7)
16 Lake of impressive size and saline in a bizarre way (6,3)
17 Again, unfortunate spouse needs relief from battering (8)
19 First gear? (7)
21 Note – biting insect around north is prevalent (7)
22 The Spanish, in big trouble start complaining it's to do with another country (6)
24 Mount drive-off point within the borders of Scotland (5)

3

ACROSS

1 Peas burnt so cooked these (4-7)
9 Left a note behind (4)
10 Focus attention on the juice extract (11)
11 Fuss, when it's cooler? (4)
14 Ranger employed to clean the pans (7)
16 Whereon to rest, or toss about (6)
17 Observe no English chums can be found in bloomers (6)
18 The curse of medicine? (11,4)
19 She's a lute-player travelling west and without a bed (6)
21 Until let free, first owl inside is to keep hooting (6)
22 His smile seen to irritate, mid-point (7)
23 May be drawn but could be lost (4)
26 Sharp-pointed sticks for prodding and old-fashioned confinement to go after penal reform (11)
27 Continue, stupid! (4)
28 Dali on art? It confuses the conventional (11)

DOWN

2 Kind of crop that is pulled up, in consequence (4)
3 Pinch and scratch (4)
4 Escaping, though not for example, shot, still loses his head (6)
5 Novel character with whom we are both intimate (3,6,6)
6 It's upsetting, these endless taxes (6)
7 Roman poet's combative skills (7,4)
8 Fairground attraction where rifles are deployed (6-5)
12 I poach large game in the Aegean (11)
13 Come top in it? (11)
14 Takes a walk – or goes fishing in a boat (7)
15 Creator, in a way, of one sort of power (7)
20 Writer who exemplifies 14 down (6)
21 Worry tin-opener may be required for the afternoon refreshment (3-3)
24 None cut return game (4)
25 Putting other birds to flight? (4)

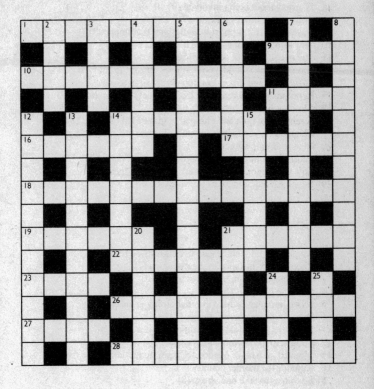

4

ACROSS

4 Worried about being involved (9)
8 Plant taking litre of mixture (7)
9 Gave one's full support to something that flopped? (7)
10 This bird is migrant – locate it out East (4-3)
11 The masses are not so significant? (9)
13 A set of steps around a pole, it goes above the door (8)
14 Leave high and dry in London (6)
17 Relinquish key taken away from princely foreign house (7)
19 Clothing hard to throw off? (6)
23 A rabbit is put out and charged to graze? Bit off, that! (8)
25 Chopped up vegetables for staff of office at a party in Spain (9)
26 Neat sounding agreement (7)
27 Shortfall requires skilful handling here in France (7)
28 Low rent negotiated, admitted, for old headgear (7)
29 Infer cash handout gains the vote (9)

DOWN

1 Angle part of machine-gun over this dried food (9)
2 Recovers for instance in the monsoon (7)
3 Keep close to team leader for a time (9)
4 Grab the chickens (6)
5 Move into place where internal piping is the end! (8)
6 Rose found on country walks (7)
7 Penniless individual entertaining me is a poet (7)
12 To turn to the person with the seat (7)
15 Medical assistance needed for team flung out into the river (9)
16 Ruin for the mother country (9)
18 So thin as to take one aback (8)
20 A partner on centre-court's a raw beginner? Could be! (7)
21 Spaniard heading off Russian (7)
22 Going around Iran, perhaps, encountered this tower (7)
24 Suit to change into (6)

5

ACROSS

4 Stop the current flow (8)
8 Licence for vehicle free of all charges (6)
9 Tricky tide's trapped people – expected to sink to the bottom! (8)
10 Quartet upset repeatedly by women's fancy embellishment (4-4)
11 Small bird on boy painter (6)
12 Material that comes from the Bath area (8)
13 Books of the month – a sell-out (8)
16 Many too advanced in years to get insurance protection (8)
19 My apology, none the less, for more than one partner (8)
21 Throwing off vest, plunge in a river – fast (6)
23 Pupil the gray tossed, suffering from this? (8)
24 Bridal shower (8)
25 Crime of harming one fly? (6)
26 Hide is from where you can see the early cuckoo (8)

DOWN

1 A good distance, but not too far perhaps, for a drive (7)
2 Bring on fit, lacking the antidote (9)
3 A stiffener for good man with halo, possibly, over top of head (6)
4 Rules I can copy in order to obtain this document (9,6)
5 A composer (8)
6 The sky? (5)
7 Brown rat disturbed by a blast of music (7)
14 A huge ball might be ridiculous (9)
15 Inventor of plate for a sound cuppa? (8)
17 Issue of consequence (7)
18 Fancy a gin and lime, somehow, but get left out (7)
20 Caused an explosion but pardoned (6)
22 Is the engineer suitable to do the job? (5)

6

ACROSS

1 Animals are increasing, we hear, in swampy areas (8)
5 I am taking a long time forming concepts (6)
9 Have greatest number of offspring after all (8)
10 Live round the artillery put into her (6)
12 At home, an infant needs love, entirely (2,4)
13 Supporters with guns hemming in the others (3-5)
15 Italian court throwing out this speech-making process (12)
18 Aiming weapon at owl on flat opposite? (12)
23 Jewellery used medicinally? (3-5)
24 Screening last word I caught on return trip (6)
26 Requiring money to get something to eat in the pub? (6)
27 Expressing surprise at the beginning (8)
28 The egg, for example, yokel's thrown at old copper (6)
29 Tradesman who passes on the account? (8)

DOWN

1 Magician's bird (6)
2 Early activity in West End to acquire freehold land (6)
3 Pack-horse has rump set out of joint (7)
4 Rent reduced by a pound, so relax (4)
6 Grim end to half-hearted song leads to feverish complaint (7)
7 Wins assistance when opposed (8)
8 No encore to this rendering! (4-4)
11 Court disaster, working – landing up in the soup (7)
14 The dignitaries associated with crooks (7)
16 May bless reformed flock (8)
17 Song made over gear crazy boy put on (8)
19 Cloth limit intake of English and other church members (7)
20 Rising fury over rate change in Africa (7)
21 Judge indisposed to have another pint? (6)
22 Hound or hound's prey (6)
25 Point to litter-holder – it's an eyesore (4)

7

ACROSS

4 Caption is ingenious, including it (8)
8 Deteriorated, it's said, over a long period (6)
9 Smelling a rat, the Spaniard snarled (8)
10 Not the main track for the team (4-4)
11 Being close to the listener, win favour (6)
12 Feeble member of the family with the nervous twitch (8)
13 Partly prevented deer fouling reed (8)
16 Cry of course will make us aware of imminent shot (8)
19 Cardinal point (8)
21 Does change include copper coin? (6)
23 Sanity exemplified by girl embracing idiot, but without love (8)
24 High-ranking lady starting to eat centre-piece at table (8)
25 Performed war dance – and he took part (6)
26 Dresser ought to be set off, with them (3,5)

DOWN

1 Has its point in figured work (7)
2 Throw her a towel by the pool (9)
3 Got fire going again around the reactor core – thus, an old widow! (6)
4 To become taller, take exercise (7,4,4)
5 Always turning up? (3,5)
6 Just ticked over, though I had been in front (5)
7 Badly leaking connection (7)
14 Duck and swallow under cover (9)
15 Celebrates vehicles crossing the river (8)
17 Former pupils smoke – why, it isn't clear (7)
18 Ducks taxes without hesitation (7)
20 Makes slow progress of some feet (6)
22 Someone to bring the lady to us (5)

8

ACROSS

1 Old-fashioned instruments for playing the blues (8)
5 Slip up, here? No, down (3,3)
9 To put it briefly, cheat the stupid (8)
10 A soldier in trouble for moving slowly (6)
12 Advantage taken upon getting lost in a way (3,2)
13 Compensation for withdrawal of book about fifty top union employees (9)
14 Having second thoughts about aged leader, shot and now stretched out on the floor (6-6)
18 Female relative drunk on old English port: food called for (4,8)
21 It fills the gap under tile that's worked loose (9)
23 Undressed kid (5)
24 New development more by accident (6)
25 Devotee of the weed giving tonic mixture to a Scot (8)
26 Kicking, I net ball somehow? Good! (6)
27 Clutch a boy providing food (3,5)

DOWN

1 Pole on the way up – within a month gets the title (6)
2 Allow nothing to go up above the door (6)
3 Pries deep into these parts of the organ (4-5)
4 I'm taking off with skinhead truant enamoured with crime (12)
6 Large antelope all over Zambia going for plant with edible roots (5)
7 With jagged slashes deployed dagger and disembowelled lady (8)
8 Time to dine on stew (8)
11 Poor Dora's most unhappy in this job (4-8)
15 Cast off sons trace long-lost relatives (9)
16 So noisy, it's beginning to scare fish in the river (8)
17 Log movement of sun overhead – it's wobbling! (8)
19 Realise, unfortunately, there's no point in the story being continued (6)
20 Enclosed as written (6)
22 Fish with a slice of onion is synthetic (5)

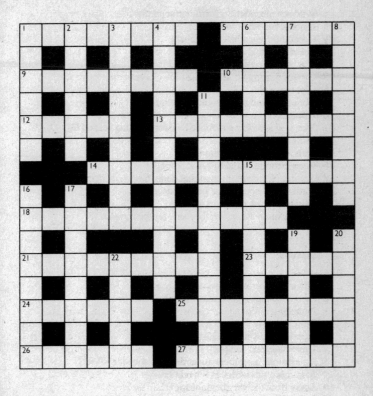

9

ACROSS

1 Wild screams about a fearful atrocity (8)
5 I should be, when small (6)
9 Odorous? React fast! (8)
10 Takes a duck aboard (6)
12 The bird is roosting inside the hide (6)
13 Groups beating up squatter (8)
15 Clot like a plot? (7)
16 Not much land but of sound promise (4)
20 Bite lip (4)
21 Moves at speed to go around everyone, taking second in parking (7)
25 Falls, due to eye problem (8)
26 Extra effort required to get out of it (6)
28 The case for getting something done (6)
29 Birds who disrupted the performance (4-4)
30 Painter at work on lathe? (6)
31 A route more attractive, they say, for the traveller (8)

DOWN

1 Gloomy elk crossing the river (6)
2 Said to change a good man into a bad one (6)
3 Nobody left unscathed? (3,5)
4 Split lease (4)
6 Appeal for dismissal causing uproar (6)
7 Cross about art and poetry (8)
8 Catastrophe after there are changes in star side (8)
11 Massage a girl with this illness (7)
14 Score from the very beginning (7)
17 Inclination to write a song (8)
18 Tag along with a riot stirred up by him (8)
19 Cockney's full set of dentures, he says, tickles the palate (8)
22 Cutting a ring in the wood (6)
23 Laundress on tap (6)
24 Rain gauge (6)
27 A female one's a butter producer (4)

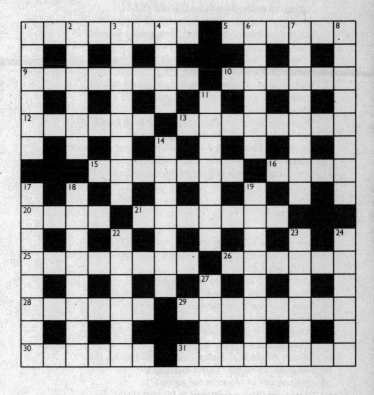

10

ACROSS

1 Old master ordered vindaloo and rice (8,2,5)
9 Quick gin cocktail, with no food to follow (7)
10 Single Scotsman – one credited with great wisdom (7)
11 A knot to avoid when sailing? (4)
12 Gnashing teeth, I clap this form of communication (10)
13 Female duck roosts in the trees (7)
15 Walked upon? Behave correctly, going back to study (7)
17 Enthusiastic approval by current demand (7)
19 Settle the will (7)
20 Shows resolution – endures abstinence from food (6,4)
22 May hold medicine – sounds disgusting (4)
25 A giddy goat has eaten it – orchestrating great excitement (7)
26 Is forgiving about money sent in error (7)
27 Supernatural beings just teased my other dog (5-10)

DOWN

1 One of those who go in for long sentences (5)
2 Concerned with appearance of new issue (9)
3 Biting wth a specific force (4)
4 Look sharp – when they are drawn (7)
5 Drop of French perfume (7)
6 Book transport to see wonders of nature (9)
7 Female insect? (5)
8 In no way, we hear, could this be to blame (9)
13 Pole planting irises by the river (9)
14 Relax – article is in Andes, in litter container (5,4)
16 Flirtation leading to many a marriage (9)
18 Outcast, so I'm of a criminal group (7)
19 Conductor mounts it or rises to play the piano (7)
21 A small party I claim in court (5)
23 Rolls produced by rolls (5)
24 Smooth tyre that's useless (4)

11

ACROSS

1 Take exercise and become taller? (7,4,4)
9 Naughty schoolboys' improper behaviour (3,4)
10 Boy needing a vitamin (7)
11 Pirate docked – having to take an erratic course (4)
12 Blood-hound savaging the hungry dark corgi I lost (7-3)
13 Foreign dignitaries in shipwreck east of California (7)
15 Praise a variegated flowering shrub (7)
17 Put out of office in whirlwind clean-up (7)
19 Feasts in right royal fashion on last of sandwiches (7)
20 O412C! (5,5)
22 Record, when objections are withdrawn (4)
25 I organised date outside church, for a drink (4,3)
26 The lass, carelessly, has unprotected locks (7)
27 Complaint spelled out in station register (15)

DOWN

1 Just like a judge? (5)
2 Peer loved to demolish, then rebuild (9)
3 Perhaps saw sack lifted (4)
4 In skeleton form, it sounds likely to provoke laughter (7)
5 Subtle differences sun can bring about, in a way (7)
6 Rubber tree outside botanical gardens has a bit missing – pinning in position is required (9)
7 Strayed right into reed bog (5)
8 Old times (4-5)
13 Collapsing, seek support in endless dance (9)
14 Tricky type takes parking place for taxi on street, then returns (9)
16 Gardener's ration (9)
18 Almost go to settle in another country – here, for example (7)
19 Chatter from poorly-assembled device (7)
21 Parts of the Far East (5)
23 I get in fish as a main ingredient (5)
24 Brilliant, raising animals (4)

12

ACROSS

1 Witty exchanges about golfing terms (8)
5 Creature seen from one in boat going round the point (3-3)
9 Hawker with no wares to sell (8)
10 Beastly article received by mail order (6)
12 Birds for example disturbed rest (6)
13 The case of the black-leg poet (8)
15 Stretches of greenery thrips have half demolished, in border (6,6)
18 Apocalyptic group of riders (4,8)
23 Painter, late starter then prophet (8)
24 Tend to pause, in headlong rush (6)
26 Boy is holding book – a sex manual? (6)
27 Strong feelings caused by transfer charges (8)
28 Metal turned colour – it's highly combustible (6)
29 Forecasts appearing in the papers – about time! (8)

DOWN

1 Beam and post at bottom of river (6)
2 Chum to make the attempt? It's not worth serious consideration (6)
3 Bird on its perch? (7)
4 Seek sport supplements (4)
6 Give the subject a title (7)
7 Camping out in a military operation (8)
8 In stampede, damaged shawl I'd wrapped round daughter (4,4)
11 Break up – cast off better half (7)
14 Keep an eye on position of bishop (7)
16 Fateful mix-up in opening number making one flush (8)
17 Refuse to go below (4,4)
19 As a last resort calls for money (7)
20 In the Mid-West a mistake gets past (7)
21 Fit a particular environment and live to a great age? (6)
22 King George, specifically a rider, takes it in (6)
25 Piano tune suitable for a duet (4)

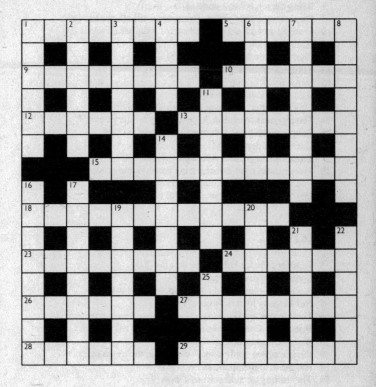

13

ACROSS

1 Being clever, score a point (4)
3 Preposterous triad claim – wanting to kill off mother (10)
10 Coming down from difficult ascent right beside a lake (9)
11 Faulty ignition (5)
12 Plant article on the inn-keeper (5)
13 Compulsion to acquire fourth estate by a river (8)
15 Game for poor players (7)
17 Glib talk about one sort of dog (7)
19 This supporter's in favour of parking mine first (3-4)
21 The physical condition brought on by military duty (7)
22 Simple collection? Just one simple song (8)
24 Circulation manager (5)
27 Tree, very large, that is found by river (5)
28 Meeting this right inside during preservation process (9)
29 Pull them out in church and the recital's over? (5-5)
30 Obscenity making stomachs turn! (4)

DOWN

1 Teacher falls for holiday excursions (5-5)
2 Signs of approval for parasites (5)
4 A support – very good – turns up, by the way (7)
5 Her Majesty in car, waves (7)
6 Thunderous applause (5)
7 Does such a smile make one defenceless? (9)
8 With pole, get duck up waterfall (4)
9 Realise rotten apple-core is wedged in the trellis (8)
14 Have one nightcap too many? (5,5)
16 The drilling outside is an irritation (9)
18 In earthquake, duck – being by nature a coward (4-4)
20 Press it furiously – again and again (7)
21 Promise Alf made to raise his hat (4,3)
23 Peer into storehouse – nothing! (5)
25 A team order that goes without saying (5)
26 One point, playing loo? Another game! (4)

14

ACROSS

1 Seaweed on the menu? (4,4)
5 Beret student with a cold rejected for sheepskin hat (6)
9 Deaf thing? (8)
10 North American, one of sixteen on the board, holds duplicate key (6)
12 Follow play about this period (6)
13 Held a map out – to read by it? (8)
15 Near Paris: ominous diversion (12)
18 Composer's works meeting the bill, say? (12)
23 The altruism of folk (8)
24 Season well (6)
26 Following the herd, ring-leader gets stuck into the port (6)
27 Vase and jar broken by ball? Capital! (8)
28 Stop press news: Lawrence in final! (6)
29 Commendation for provision of water supply (4,4)

DOWN

1 Retiring a little way, after a fashion (6)
2 Is nothing to prevent formation of same pressure group (6)
3 Ambassador taking time off to get a document (7)
4 As has been stated, this is just tolerable (2-2)
6 An evil foreign banker – the Devil himself (7)
7 Military headquarters where, locked up, suffering's endless (8)
8 Money-saving way to carry primate in coffer (8)
11 Classify it the ultimate insect (7)
14 Pears tumbling to the grass (7)
16 Slope had to be bulldozed to accommodate this plant (8)
17 Crush and leave in fury (5,3)
19 Gloomy on the point, except in certain circumstances (7)
20 Old master beat girl up (7)
21 Tree-roots cut back by dramatist (6)
22 Turn a blind eye to distressed region (6)
25 Stop losing head, and relax (4)

15

ACROSS

4 Champion to have a meal, with stout (9)
8 Pip, a heavy weight, gets direction to become thinner (7)
9 Tips for working out gains (7)
10 One's own doesn't sound a modest note (7)
11 I'm found in Eastern firm worthy of respect (9)
13 Custard pie thrown first at a vehicle (8)
14 Article on pine, similar to a litchi (6)
17 Make a hit with the gear? (7)
19 Sail around and around Britain with a dog (6)
23 Lots of whippings! (8)
25 Checked the pipe outside the closet (9)
26 Could it be his hallucination started because of this? (7)
27 Averts disaster in student journeys (7)
28 Military men repeatedly hold out – now send them another way (7)
29 Sway, and in fen, uncle, losing direction goes astray (9)

DOWN

1 Gigantic beasts – get pig-food round, fellows! (9)
2 Drive back through pure chaos to the university (7)
3 Bird with flower on its head? Rubbish! (9)
4 Dog going into burrow with reluctance (6)
5 A little bit of journalism on the quiet (8)
6 Abstain from taking the air (7)
7 A girl to give the game away in a rough sea (7)
12 Rising doubts, having bled endlessly, though apparently it was not a close shave (7)
15 Gold box military force gives musicians (9)
16 Novel point on cover for retirement in this publication? (4-5)
18 It's just the thing for chaps! (3-5)
20 Maize protein supplied by our Lena (7)
21 Sort out a French composer (7)
22 Island opposed to a half-month return (7)
24 Stick plug in this spot (6)

16

ACROSS

1 Face up – but not to the challenge (4,4)
5 Bedroom window? (6)
9 Insect you find on the golf-course? (8)
10 Aircraft, a great many, got rid of (6)
12 State article boy split, reversing (6)
13 Centipede? There's countless number around the post-office (8)
15 To get the information, ply clientele with gin (12)
18 Entire tax too ridiculously over the top! (12)
23 Ready skill needed to fly around it, with aircraftman and myself as passengers (8)
24 Bad smell climber found is from cattle (6)
26 Put in charge again (6)
27 Can label the Spanish put on be this castle? (8)
28 I tarry out of curiosity (6)
29 Pale, quaking, with greatly reduced visibility right inside vault (4-4)

DOWN

1 Ask somebody to go away (6)
2 Quit after start of Conservative split (6)
3 In Scotland, there's a lot of noise beyond the sandhill (7)
4 Fit source? (4)
6 Opportunity to start? (7)
7 Will this sort of youth ensure you can avoid getting locked up? (8)
8 Cures engineers, at first sight about to perish (8)
11 Dreadful weather conditions when there's no going uphill in bike ride (7)
14 Stopping – for the dentist – does not mean he does this (7)
16 Mariner's fears are modified (3-5)
17 Using cane on student with hesitation? Not if he's one for discipline! (8)
19 Bombast about Samuel's teacher being dependent on it (7)
20 Wet spot, perhaps, on the floor (3-4)
21 Note in cruise-ship to postpone voyage (6)
22 Rhyming prosthesis (3-3)
25 Clamp-down on immorality? (4)

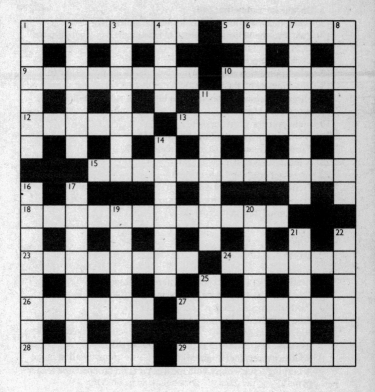

17

ACROSS

1 Back it for a come-back (4)
3 Colombian river fish – we object to the bones (10)
10 Two disturbed characters about to assault girl – to what purpose? (7,2)
11 Looking for post (5)
12 Jolly companion aboard (5)
13 Join trickster on the brink (8)
15 Large pores damage point to this unpleasant skin condition (7)
17 Bone from Munster (7)
19 Light pole for sitting upon (7)
21 Disturb something covered by stone (7)
22 Farm-worker seen to attack her daughter (8)
24 A moss-strewn island (5)
27 An insect gripping large tree (5)
28 Two men of a bygone era (9)
29 Persistent noise adjacent to river in this part of England (10)
30 The animal that's close (4)

DOWN

1 Let down girl about to go into inferior position (5,5)
2 Cast provides support for injured member (5)
4 Partly overhear a chemist's complaint (7)
5 Sums relatives hold a short time (7)
6 Hinged stone? (5)
7 Irishman at first travelling in Goa, now here (9)
8 Southern river, for certain (4)
9 A burning issue – daily with local circulation dropped first leader (8)
14 Chap scattered mail around – with this objective (10)
16 A favourite part on stage accepted by male lead with spirit (9)
18 Issue from key embassy (8)
20 Hands out food in the week, but tries to avoid it (7)
21 Gave evidence of leader held by count (7)
23 Topic for discussion thrown into the melting pot (5)
25 Sounds like the cereal of the month (5)
26 Little Welsh composer (4)

18

ACROSS

4 Traveller needs tow back at first light to English town (8)
8 It's fitted together, causing leaf damage (6)
9 A warning to those who come after (4-4)
10 Vehicle doctor in a fury reverses, in the plant (8)
11 Detesting sort of trick in force (6)
12 I'd lost sight of some of the troops (8)
13 Music that's peaceful, though with commercial break (8)
16 Personal appearance before change of scene (8)
19 Sibyl's speciality – working cypher operation (8)
21 Author making unhurried progress (6)
23 Scotsman taken in by bird in Cumbria (8)
24 Ignore a feast (8)
25 Move fast after take-off (6)
26 Place in Scotland for a man with more than one wife (8)

DOWN

1 Thus, Islam disorientated these Afro-Asians (7)
2 What a pity such wrinkles are unbecoming (4,5)
3 The rascal I understand is providing fish (6)
4 European farm-workers going to the dogs (6,9)
5 Hide is in the field by the railway (8)
6 Admittance to more sheltered water (5)
7 Dressed like a judge, Her Majesty was boring (7)
14 Right name for a frightening experience (9)
15 In conclusion, the tomb inscription may be (8)
17 A politician in a fury going on it? (7)
18 Disreputable affair wherein lads can get involved (7)
20 Attack, or shun changes (6)
22 Thought a head would be a tail? (5)

19

ACROSS

1 View of girl flanked by her parents (8)
5 Maybe plane's in the way, by the way (6)
9 Suitable gear for a Cortina (8)
10 Supports lawful crackdown, but only partially (6)
12 Palm seen next, by a river (6)
13 Dog giving a last snarl at man (8)
15 Fern conceals ten grouse, dad! (6-6)
18 In this seat he counts your change (7,5)
23 It hinders production of best coal (8)
24 Instruction to players confused a lot, for example (6)
26 Passengers certainly would, if the bus were! (6)
27 Fire getting out of control in the breeze, she's found (8)
28 Remarkable piece of railway equipment (6)
29 Sacred greeting to those joined in matrimony (8)

DOWN

1 Equality for one in the group (6)
2 Nose is distressed? Surely they should affect the ear? (6)
3 Boy's free to net fish (7)
4 Have despicable intent? (4)
6 Travel firm receiving brief answer – gets the bird (7)
7 Graven images? Chins get wagging (8)
8 River holds fresh water, they learn (8)
11 Flower with or without the vessel (7)
14 To direct into a different channel will take engineers an age (7)
16 Start to cheer following them to get an award (8)
17 Youngster trade-unionists throw out (8)
19 Cart-wheeling ambassador leading actor to the tube (7)
20 It's not the usual thing to have drinks containing ice served up (7)
21 Pole and shaft lacking width (6)
22 Base where very good side performed (6)
25 Mineral of chemical extract (4)

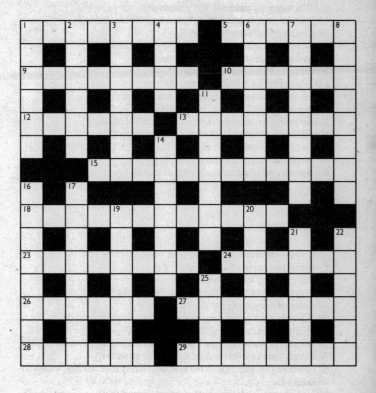

20

ACROSS

4 He's requiring privacy? Moor the boat by the point (9)
8 In a matter of sex, I allow vulgar take-off at the start (7)
9 A red tap provides the connection (7)
10 Lucan? My, that could be malicious representation! (7)
11 I get at one in order to make a bargain (9)
13 Vehicle I parked by the hut disappeared (8)
14 Gear to catch retreating animal (6)
17 Tar mark causing discoloration? Keep off it! (7)
19 Play ending before time, at certain times (6)
23 Hot tears generated by this electrical device (8)
25 Side battles with southern team for small cup (9)
26 Can't recall having it (7)
27 Swear it's not poetry I'm turning in (7)
28 Sewage emerging here – it's full to a fault! (7)
29 Fluff from river birds and swallow (9)

DOWN

1 Find record above your head? (9)
2 Writer has to sleep on the heather (7)
3 Girl claiming to be boy lifting the sack (9)
4 Any elk would be knocked out by this gas (6)
5 Roller-skating equipment? (8)
6 Traveller isn't commonly required to put on another coat (7)
7 Entertainment revealing lunatic art in you (7)
12 Tried so desperately to be book-makers (7)
15 Trendy firm I got in trouble, using false name (9)
16 Favouring neither side in the war used lively tune to bring troops to order (9)
18 Using a special permit, newsman got around it (8)
20 Overseer? (7)
21 Ran mile, perhaps, to train people (7)
22 Some winds that arrive annually from the East upset Scots lad (7)
24 Ambassador and academic receiving first-aid following this collision (4-2)

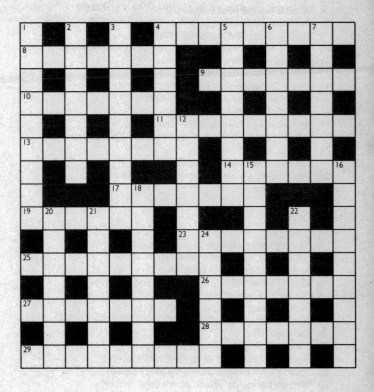

21

ACROSS

4 In fields beyond what is spoken (8)
8 Twice jump over piece on board (6)
9 One blend can be distinguished (8)
10 These kind of stockings appear to be smaller, they say (8)
11 Palm giving shade to desert (6)
12 Tradesman who could have helped those nursery-rhyme mice? (8)
13 A vice set the wrong way can raise blister (8)
16 Promises made by witches to worker (8)
19 Lead on! I have burst leg vein (8)
21 Hun seen to go towards it, then turn tail (6)
23 In this vessel I leave Hanoi, travelling to a Channel Isle (5,3)
24 Masters visit our doctor (8)
25 Settled on unlimited prayer (6)
26 This creature sat outside the vessel? Right inside! (5-3)

DOWN

1 You can safely tell them to go to blazes (7)
2 Fake illness, say, to get a drink (9)
3 Attraction of another hearing? (6)
4 Tips off about booking for someone keen on saving (15)
5 Direction to take off everything but this garment (3-5)
6 Journey round the world, or part of it (5)
7 A title social worker set aside (7)
14 Cat-killer (9)
15 Lover wheeling a pram round old city (8)
17 Draft of something to say at your exit? (7)
18 Such an obvious error provoking angry frowns (7)
20 With six having the resources, it's practicable (6)
22 For making carpet tiles, maybe (5)

22

ACROSS

1 One who works by hand gives strain to a politician from the London area (10)
6 Strikes back in a fight (4)
9 Possessions which bring someone gold (5)
10 Quarrel with a politician concerning type of tenure (9)
12 It is the place of instruction to keep soldiers calm, we hear (7,6)
14 The plane crash is caused by a heavy creature (8)
15 Changes about in being like a cone (6)
17 Seaman who gives a mark to a beginner (6)
19 Beats her badly, but shows signs of life (8)
21 The one who finishes off an aristocrat behind the trees is new to crime (5,10)
24 Language in which noun operates strangely (9)
25 I competed like Bacchus (5)
26 Run for the line (4)
27 Constant spirit shown in the game (10)

DOWN

1 The prophet turns up for a drink (4)
2 A man with a drink inside is company (7)
3 Performer who puts painting up in view with a sound of sea and mountain (8,5)
4 Abstains from music (8)
5 Author who sounds as if he is a budding one (5)
7 Be stimulating and demonstrate the truth without approval (7)
8 Being in the same suit, they cause embarrassment at court (5,5)
11 When newly married I chant for the priest (13)
13 Dispose of some property in Cumbria (10)
16 Where to express displeasure about part of the course being taken up (8)
18 Punishment as a sign of rank (7)
20 Brave girl in this place holding nothing in (7)
22 Bird places foot on island (5)
23 Poems held in good esteem (4)

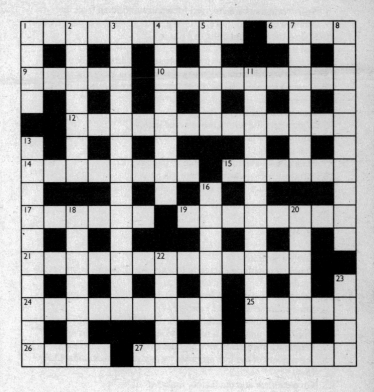

23

ACROSS

1 Still dream lives are changed for a second (6,9)
9 Finish with record-maker caught and confined to a certain area (7)
10 Vale artist has something to paint in (7)
11 Got up as a flower (4)
12 Release from punishment when there are wild lions about (10)
13 He is invested with land, when Edward starts away in charge (7)
15 Plant which enables one to read superficially before the intention is reversed (7)
17 Jackets for smokers? (7)
19 What a bird did with a broken reed pen (7)
20 Hardy fellow is to speculate about the returned party note (10)
22 War spoils (4)
25 Do a turn awkwardly in a kind of building (7)
26 Informer who gives back a story in a bar (7)
27 Royal accommodation is kept separate in announcements (5,10)

DOWN

1 Control an animal (5)
2 There is something attractive in a number of poems being set to music (9)
3 Trees a novice planted in town (4)
4 Strange horse without a carriage (7)
5 Broken out and used although obedient (7)
6 One tailless animal in a row provides something to drive (9)
7 People who appear in nice nighties (5)
8 A company of the line provided by a group of irregular soldiers? (5-4)
13 Give the sack and the factory makes trouble (9)
14 Fish in the country to make oneself independent (4-5)
16 Woody place could give a chap a healthy colour if hatless (9)
18 A note from paper to politician, it gives one a healthy look (7)
19 He makes his appeal in a front page article (7)
21 Duck as it goes into port (5)
23 Afflictions come a second after love returns (5)
24 Election candidate needs a key to this squalid housing (4)

24

ACROSS

1 Where rackets are used to crush the law? (6,5)
10 Issues it in town (5)
11 Groups which distribute the company rations (9)
12 Create a mistaken impression that the spy-master is playing well (9)
13 Abhor a vacuum (5)
14 Warning to skaters? (6)
16 First a bun is cut up and had for tea (8)
18 One who cares for animals would be broken-hearted if he lost a large number (8)
20 Predicament caused by fighting with the English (6)
23 Product of a western summer? (5)
24 Glow of anger during the journey (9)
26 If a virgin embraces a single soldier it will soon disappear (9)
27 A thousand is put before the Queen by a mean person (5)
28 Plant to spoil a display round a London street (11)

DOWN

2 Leaves without owing anything (5)
3 Poison which makes part of the body almost pleasant (7)
4 Bully for ancient hero! (6)
5 People enter it not prepared for dressing (8)
6 Anger about excessive rise in striking (7)
7 How locks are arranged so that the water stays in motion? (9,4)
8 Something in the chemistry may make one in love with tarts (8)
9 First major score made by a girl over a long period (6,7)
15 Cross when the rest collapse and are about to declare (8)
17 Novel plants of invasive habit (8)
19 Hate turning over terrorists, being a girl-friend (7)
21 Ring me during the visit for something used in medicine (7)
22 Examination which gives little money to the runner-up (6)
25 Zest which is nothing more than wind (5)

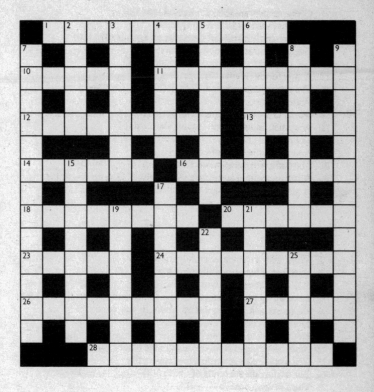

25

ACROSS

1 Commercial transport of reliable kind (5-5)
8 An artist's love – mixed-up type (4)
10 Declare getting together can unite an organisation (10)
11 Her make-up is in rainbow colours! (4)
13 Lecture about retaining correspondence (7)
15 A way to split labour (6)
16 The probationer one cannot fault (6)
17 Warm-hearted? (9,6)
18 Dreadful sloven as depicted in fiction (6)
20 A woman entering trains to this standard (6)
21 Longed for time to take wildlife refuge over (7)
22 A speedy little beast of course (4)
25 The band will accept drinks – there's a revelation! (5-5)
26 A requirement of some magazine editors (4)
27 A girl's more rambling and garbled tales (10)

DOWN

2 Work with a trainee assembling jewellery (4)
3 Puts on the better-qualified teaching staff (4)
4 "X" is to acquire a river holding (6)
5 Let it all go to pot, making money – such a dangerous thing! (1,6,8)
6 On retirement, no-one thanks Northern people (6)
7 His intelligence is available to anybody for a little cash (4-6)
9 Determined to take gun in through lounge (10)
12 Stars never move from one side to the other (10)
13 The Tory leader interrupts too, apparently (7)
14 For writing on the home of music? (7)
15 Used to keep time (6-4)
19 Dry and stony hill area (6)
20 Situation a woman wanted (6)
23 Drop round for some food (4)
24 Present a man goes on about (4)

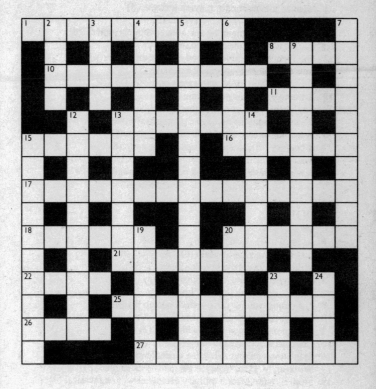

26

ACROSS

1 Musical instruction for playing toccatas (8)
5 Foreign article discovered in food (6)
9 He'll make complaint by and about people in general (8)
10 Caught a girl on the rebound (6)
12 The French look for somebody to rent the property (6)
13 Acts as arbitrator – deems it a mistake (8)
15 Substitute train for strap-hangers only? (8-4)
18 Attractive recording equipment! (8,4)
23 One's curt when correct, showing resolve (8)
24 It's sanctimonious to judge a plagiarist (6)
26 Some flair is essential for arranging flowers (6)
27 A country person about 50 can be charming (8)
28 Query put inside bag that's for packing (6)
29 American cash held by bank not very long ago (8)

DOWN

1 Alone with the Sun, see? (6)
2 Just about making St-Malo (6)
3 Willing to accept the burden (7)
4 Person getting into knots causing a row (4)
6 A point a top man finds exciting (7)
7 A mounted soldier can overturn one on firing (8)
8 Fine an employee taking part (8)
11 Putting intelligence first – a bloomer (7)
14 Quite an unreliable old thing (7)
16 Make a song about twit using a needle (8)
17 Working for others, they'll get nice break in time (8)
19 From the start certain military personnel will be fanatical (7)
20 A church official, parking on the verge, had a meal (7)
21 The man who's learned a vehicle may be left in the street (6)
22 People of some standing get a key to the door (6)
25 Spend unwisely, being depressed (4)

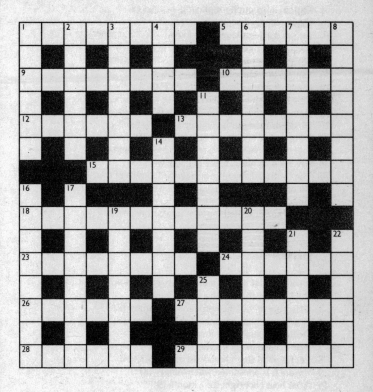

27

ACROSS

1 Military uniform for woman in prison (8)
5 Half-loves becoming cleaner (6)
10 Adult spoils and wastes away (9)
11 Become acquainted with king by name (5)
12 Searches for somewhere which no longer exists (5)
13 Sample of a setter being wrong (9)
14 Cut back like a ditch in the grass (10)
17 This is one story, but two could be taken either way (4)
19 Having lost his head, the amateur is finished (4)
20 Do deeds fit to provide material for the bards (10)
22 Be nostalgic about cars before church (9)
24 Present the chest after a hundred has been removed (5)
26 River which needs to try to make work (5)
27 The furthest away may be disposed to muster too (9)
28 Bit of grammar which helps to make a stranger understand the language (6)
29 Where to get something soothing before an exam (8)

DOWN

1 It sounds as if having meals is a protection from rain (7-8)
2 Replay concerned with a bit of cricket (5)
3 Offspring of violence produced by farmer (8)
4 Now mother has gone the dog is obstinate (5)
6 Dedicated person is flattened (6)
7 Pole needed to get flowers over the river (9)
8 Let England share broadcast opera (6,3,6)
9 Ensure it is consumed when hungry (8)
15 After heat I act right for a month (9)
16 Approach which makes food ready to eat (4-4)
18 Dream I go crazy, being a character (8)
21 Agreement for a second among the workers (6)
23 Run in next race (5)
25 Beginner enters number for meals (5)

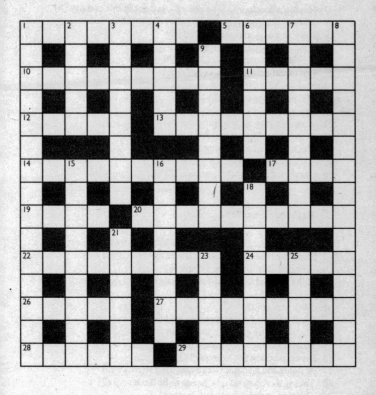

28

ACROSS

4 - Having a bearing on love poetry – but not in this country (8)
8 A sober man taken in over military show (6)
9 16, given a legal right, scoffed (8)
10 Figure the writer has a flap on (8)
11 A French lie occasioning some disquiet (6)
12 Broadcast arranged by a nun once (8)
13 Making a signal when slowing down (8)
16 The new sergeant's 9 (8)
19 The basic necessity for a suit (8)
21 An insult is of little importance (6)
23 A sad sign offering rent reduction (8)
24 The ranch had a nice appearance (8)
25 ''X'' turned in an old Greek (6)
26 Impressed by key charge made (8)

DOWN

1 Foreign money invested in sugar and pepper (7)
2 Place the Queen's given a tradesman (9)
3 Pole possibly going for a drink (6)
4 Coloured and liberated – the situation in only one part of South Africa (6,4,5)
5 Back number (8)
6 It's the Spaniard one's put up, right? (5)
7 The mechanic showing little heart is annoying (7)
14 Material being read quite wrongly (9)
15 Inside position for example (8)
17 A sailor and a social worker dancing together (7)
18 Taking a crab to bits, he needs to be dexterous (7)
20 The type inclined to show stress (6)
22 Frightful-sounding story teller (5)

29

ACROSS

1 It's essential for the traveller to approve of the wine (8)
5 Make rapid progess, always going by private transport (6)
9 Deep affection (3-2-3)
10 A delay acceptable in some degree in Spain (6)
12 Lofty for a time around one fifty (6)
13 A flower raiser's main urge (8)
15 Well-read people in constant correspondence? (3,2,7)
18 Outstanding achievement of the new market stores (12)
23 Sewers – a quarter are quite superfluous (8)
24 Trees used for pillars of the church (6)
26 No thanks to the railway official! (6)
27 Think an associate about to prepare for issue (8)
28 Clothed – and owing in consequence (6)
29 A resort named correctly in good French (8)

DOWN

1 A politician should get into step, that's plain (6)
2 Pay for example to acquire a household god (6)
3 Quietly agrees maybe to make a prediction (7)
4 In winter heather affords shelter for a bird (4)
6 A hold-up a compulsive worker finds really hard (7)
7 Cut-up over digs checks (8)
8 More rats are to be used after all (8)
11 They'll strip off for the police no longer (7)
14 Have certain law-men go over the ship (7)
16 Reputation is cardinal (8)
17 Insisted upon a dessert being cooked (8)
19 Blow up! (7)
20 Amusing a top man about some complaint (7)
21 Soldiers cannot withdraw (6)
22 Like a flighty creature getting behind (6)
25 Support for a beast (4)

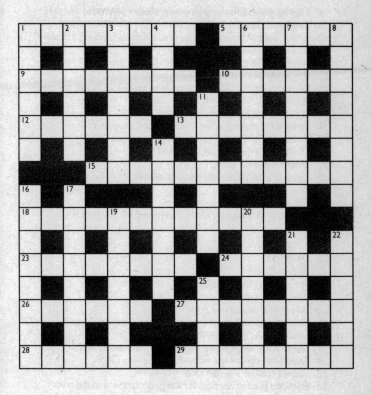

30

ACROSS

1 They help one to see, for example, about you and the girls (10)
8 Relative holds one for writer (4)
10 A wise man with space for flowers has these pioneers at heart (5-5)
11 Was accustomed to be employed (4)
13 Went into the water carrying a fish but got separated (7)
15 Girl made free with what a princess wears (6)
16 Refreshments included by those who keep open house are most attractive (6)
17 Where one plays for one's country? (8,7)
18 Reward for playing at the Oval is a food container (6)
20 It is about right that religious retreat is a fraud (6)
21 Charge made for fruit on the island (7)
22 River Don? (4)
25 Those who run the club cannot quite make a game with ten men (10)
26 Got up, we hear, as lots of eggs (4)
27 You go back without a servant to record the subject (10)

DOWN

2 Period of my early childhood (4)
3 Place left for shooting at (4)
4 Where industrious one is on edge (6)
5 Hostess who makes a team come to earth amid unusual delays (7,8)
6 Soaked as the grass above the home (6)
7 Old master caught being changed for modern artist (10)
9 Examiners sip cornets when they are runny (10)
12 Sailor I class as a spider (10)
13 Etiquette is an instrument for keeping company to the point (7)
14 Illness which would make one pass away if one didn't take the waters (7)
15 Hard labour is a vital occupation for an academic (6-4)
19 Important building where one article has to be in position (6)
20 Swear during a game? (6)
23 Deadly hill (4)
25 Male presenting a play without gin in it (4)

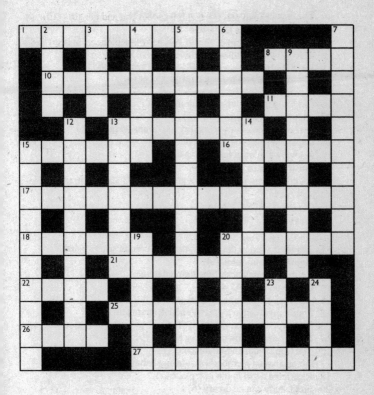

31

ACROSS

4 The usual stall to be seen at a road-side (8)
8 Simple embracing is no trick! (6)
9 Need coat in new fashion – or that's the tale (8)
10 The cat confronting a large bird intended to make a kill (8)
11 Having to walk back when there's something afoot (3-3)
12 A way to encourage the caviar-producer (8)
13 A worker in bed (8)
16 Get lit up in the club right enough! (8)
19 Amplifies general's orders (8)
21 Perfume to be returned – many find it unacceptable (6)
23 Capital support for the traveller! (4-4)
24 A lovely garden is featured in display (8)
25 Flush about the French number (6)
26 A child among children, though mature (8)

DOWN

1 Its root is used in the preparation of a certain savoury dish (7)
2 Going for restoration (9)
3 Refuse to watch absorbing comedian (6)
4 Giving no signal (7,4,4)
5 A superior's sound assistants (8)
6 Figure involved in a great Venetian stratagem (5)
7 Run over a note on evidence (7)
14 Never turning brown, so may be pine (9)
15 The beast is tall and no mistake! (8)
17 Go on about a member's disturbing behaviour (7)
18 Restricted a girl in the first place (7)
20 Field study can be dreary (6)
22 Gathers in faulty spare parts (5)

32

ACROSS

1 Contrasts, as in the set variation (10)
8 A backward island can be made efficient (4)
10 A sober man, an engineer, receiving tip for service (10)
11 Take exercise as a drug (4)
13 On the quiet some soldiers posted a donation (7)
15 A writer without money, and that's only just (6)
16 Leave the proper payment (6)
17 6 thoughts for which no directions are needed (15)
18 Bearing blossom in spring (6)
20 Plant about fifty for use in winter (6)
21 16 people fight for ascendancy (3,4)
22 Exhausting work to the Italian (4)
25 The girl not finishing with one in gaol for a serious offence (10)
26 Coarse grade (4)
27 Most grease goes off in such containers (10)

DOWN

2 Elegant beasts (4)
3 Greek character involved in a riot – a trouble-maker (4)
4 A European country without a hollow (6)
5 A ship accommodates the sailors with a bar as standard (5,3,7)
6 Back in a moment! (6)
7 Compunction about colour occupying coppers (10)
9 Broad smile possibly raised by pineapples (10)
12 Train – but not against giving up! (10)
13 Reckless gambler going into a dive? (7)
14 "X" and 8 may be maintained (7)
15 The savers set out to retain the right so they'll reap the benefit (10)
19 Harshly criticising a member of the crew (6)
20 Writing up about many a guy's separation (6)
23 Like the record? (4)
24 26 returned in a knot (4)

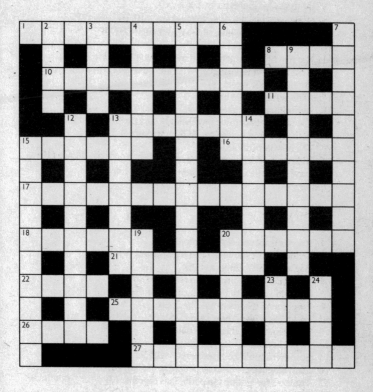

33

ACROSS

1 Rates about girls (7)
5 Old poetry that's among the crassest in all respects (7)
9 Getting mad at an inflexible arrangement (7)
10 An everyday sort of writer (7)
11 Not reaching a target, they may be fired (5,10)
12 Brazilian port is seen everywhere around the City (6)
14 Topping basic wear! (8)
17 Indians make coke here (8)
18 Doubtfully interrogate a social worker (6)
21 Speculators becoming increasingly superior? (6,3,6)
24 Weighty communication cut by a lawyer (7)
25 The new general's swell! (7)
26 A down-trodden machine-operator (7)
27 Brown, a little gentleman, won't cross the line (7)

DOWN

1 Room cleaner receiving a medal (7)
2 Unlooked-for snowfall can be a disaster! (9)
3 Bag about fifty – it's easy (5)
4 A Persian ruler some like in retrospect (6)
5 The odd vet's idea for giving a tranquilliser (8)
6 Foreigners' resorts to hold back tax (9)
7 Providing cover – how sweet! (5)
8 Man painting egghead entertainer (7)
13 At the bottom of the river? (9)
15 Fear there could be loose parts – without attachment (5-4)
16 Such language is used by people at the bar! (8)
17 The case for getting top politicians together (7)
19 To let a large number in can cause distress (7)
20 Coming changes to end VAT (6)
22 Object over the charge (5)
23 She's written a couple of letters (5)

34

ACROSS

1 Many refuse to speed (4)
3 Real estate apt to have strings attached (10)
10 Live on tea, maybe, showing a certain loftiness (9)
11 A Northerner's comeback causing shock (5)
12 Musicians' go-slow movement (5)
13 Idleness indeed! (8)
15 Checking new setting (7)
17 Feeling a book turned one on (7)
19 There's a bit of a problem in entertaining the distinguished (7)
21 Ostensible reason for a foreword? (7)
22 A letter making silly sap quite cross (8)
24 The Conservative leader, taking a breather, held on (5)
27 A way everybody can ensure a good seat at the theatre (5)
28 The simpleton is French so finds a supporter (9)
29 Bed-linen gets all twisted – in knots (5-5)
30 The head needs a lot of water (4)

DOWN

1 Flotsam and jetsam? (4,6)
2 Poles, forever short, are derisory (5)
4 The abuse of some fence (7)
5 Is able to turn round in long boat (7)
6 Laughing train-wrecker (5)
7 To do without preparation is better all round (9)
8 No choice fish! (4)
9 A girl's name of Stuart times (8)
14 Dicky sits eating eggs (10)
16 Taking fruit to fill up, figure should be trim (9)
18 Open bag up inside, being far from bright (8)
20 Note a number tucked into appropriate snack (7)
21 Bore down on a leading journalist (7)
23 A little place built entirely of tiles (5)
25 The practice of the top-drawer philosopher (5)
26 As is written repeatedly, she was once highly respected (4)

35

ACROSS

4 Rags a man breaking down – in need of sorting out! (8)
8 Get a worker to accept many an order (6)
9 Indulgence is a matter of degree (8)
10 Others drop control (8)
11 The decorative work has to be fitted in (6)
12 Service uniform with a certain air (8)
13 Pass over report for approval (8)
16 Refuse containers, trashy as can be (3-5)
19 A rogue will take one when there's exemption from penalty (8)
21 This guy had to fill up with endless bread (6)
23 Got there perhaps, but not alone (8)
24 New union members may well be showered with it (8)
25 He calls up, always without official sanction (6)
26 A sailor in smart surroundings getting under way (8)

DOWN

1 Book on the subject of benefit (7)
2 Sober study can net results (9)
3 Getting support at centre-front, played smoothly (6)
4 Light shows for politicians working late (3-5,7)
5 Misanthropic fellow in no matter what element (8)
6 Classes having a rest-break (5)
7 This island built up a militant organisation (7)
14 A pink vehicle seen before the race (9)
15 Outlaws set it facing both ways (8)
17 Deep drink taken in Dover say (7)
18 The person soaking may be more difficult to deal with (7)
20 Kept on tolling if quietly given some encouragement (6)
22 Present from Her Majesty (5)

36

ACROSS

1 A means of securing fresh linen (7-3)
8 The city's very big, see! (4)
10 Scrutinise tears in faulty bags (10)
11 A number mean to hurt (4)
13 He'll scoff at the revolutionary receiving disastrous backing (7)
15 Harry the painter framed by a woman (6)
16 A bit of muscle is required to lean over (6)
17 Night-route which may be taken at midnight (3,8,4)
18 Few appear displeased about a certain audacity (6)
20 Exotic fruit in a can – a naseberry (6)
21 Maintain there's little drink left (7)
22 Retrieved a once-fashionable dress (4)
25 Feature about a mount, a beast with a lovely coat (10)
26 In case a person swears! (4)
27 Accommodation address (3,2,5)

DOWN

2 Fifty to one it's material (4)
3 The sound is not to be turned up, note (4)
4 Got rid of deer, as destructive (6)
5 With which the writer makes his point (6-9)
6 Fish catch – could be a stone (6)
7 They're living together, though not as husband and wife (10)
9 Good man with a top position (10)
12 Fresh and amusing, and that's what people have to go on (5,5)
13 To honour debts is questionable! (7)
14 Concerning a guy employed in laboratory work (7)
15 A proposal about tax one would find an incentive (10)
19 Charges for some plants (6)
20 More artful, being an old soldier (6)
23 Insect seen leaping from leaf (4)
24 Mother a couple of scholars (4)

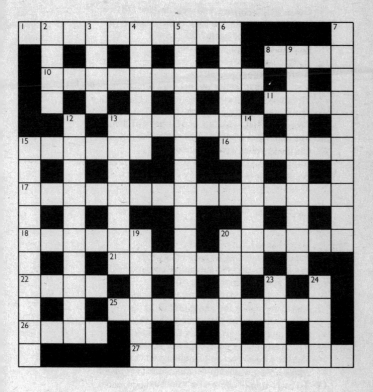

37

ACROSS

1 Good-looking homes, and well-designed (8)
5 Beats putting a portion back in the steamer! (6)
9 Went and married again? (8)
10 Fine for being caught in a pool (6)
12 Has the proper cover (6)
13 A firm ruler (8)
15 Mature Oriental sailor mixing with foreign element (12)
18 The study of man embracing woman (12)
23 The 25 one's giving for some fruit (8)
24 Gasp for breath when about 51 – not stiff though (6)
26 The odd trip is taken to show enterprise (6)
27 For the traveller's pack of cards? (8)
28 Bringing back a number of soldiers could make an impression (6)
29 Acceptable excuses given by a worker (8)

DOWN

1 Harry has to have painters in (6)
2 Panels representing an ancient city (6)
3 Went around dressed in woman's clothing (7)
4 Get together as appropriate (4)
6 Anger occasioned over a sort of art-work (7)
7 Music and dance for taking off? (3-5)
8 25 has time for the very lowest class (8)
11 Many in distress get awfully tight-fisted (7)
14 Raced around the outer edge and skidded (7)
16 Putting a good man among youngsters can cause strikes (8)
17 Make a song about almost incredible prevaricating (8)
19 To feel strongly about a lie's unusual (7)
20 A Greek maid leaves after the festivity (7)
21 The country offers a fellow a quiet retirement (6)
22 Still treats constituents badly (2,4)
25 The beast might charge one – and there's a ludicrous statement (4)

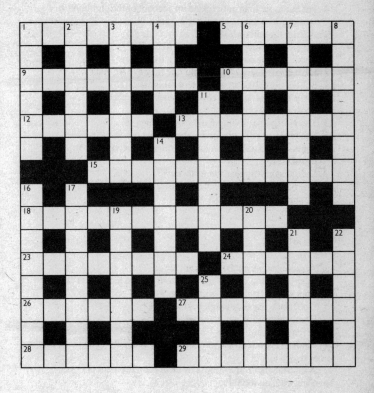

38

ACROSS

4 Put out more than anticipated on account of the children (9)
8 Bearing with a mad character's crack (7)
9 A strict moralist who's put Iran to rights (7)
10 Give information to coppers in a force (7)
11 Those raising no objection when a fool gets in (9)
13 Lie heard – a story – at the bar one may expect that (5,3)
14 Soldiers involved in the current fulmination (6)
17 They're prepared for a row whenever they meet (7)
19 Possibly showing latent ability (6)
23 The Northerner living in a depressed area (8)
25 Scattered and disappeared – about time! (9)
26 A music man accompanying the monarch needed to carry a pistol (7)
27 Loftiness can appear fun in spring (7)
28 The bank set out to be most unpleasant (7)
29 Equine understanding (5-4)

DOWN

1 Alsatians worried the attacker (9)
2 Push a boy and disturbing behaviour will be the result (7)
3 Spot outside right one is marking (9)
4 Gold trade – a very tough business (6)
5 Game allowed to get in the way (8)
6 A remover shuffled his feet, an indication of indecisiveness (7)
7 Finding French article really good about deputy-head being on the wet side (7)
12 A coastal area some choose as ideal for retirement (7)
15 Sandwich material (9)
16 No longer single-speed, that's clear (9)
18 Sportsmen may be the least affected (8)
20 Spirited instruction guiding the players (7)
21 Not slow to give voice (7)
22 Writing up different gag (7)
24 Stick notice on present (6)

39

ACROSS

1 Gets service possibly about the end of June (8)
5 The choosing of a sphere to back (6)
9 The German will carry anything for a girl (8)
10 A manufacturer no longer (6)
12 Specialist making small change in exercise (6)
13 Consequence of a cardinal's address (8)
15 Fabulous animal with head coming to a point (7)
16 Opening – using a key, it follows (4)
20 An aristocrat can turn almost clownish (4)
21 Put to death for dumping rubbish in 16! (7)
25 Flora's error – being taken in by bovine creatures (8)
26 Drapes material for display (6)
28 A guy of more than about 51 (6)
29 The craft of Gilbert and Sullivan (8)
30 A covering for sheep – and also human beings (6)
31 If properly cooked, eat green produce (8)

DOWN

1 Comparatively colourful, however one views it (6)
2 Nincompoops taking umbrage in the Civil Service (6)
3 Trendy present conservationists find essential (8)
4 Quits before nightfall (4)
6 The sum given for a horse (6)
7 Meal done, maybe get a drink (non-alcoholic) (8)
8 A great rock splits these rushing waters (8)
11 A man writing of some schemers, only to become involved (7)
14 Observer accommodating a number on strike, though not involved (7)
17 Want for nothing inside except when there's a power-failure (8)
18 Medical man admitting the ending of a life (8)
19 Check work quietly within a certain period (8)
22 State support in beer production (6)
23 Read of new capital investment (6)
24 Seeing a little notice in this place, hold on (6)
27 Beautiful, though quite thin (4)

40

ACROSS

1 Beauty treatment for a disappearing elite (9,5)
10 Although no longer a player, he insists on payment (7)
11 An imposter makes a call to arms (7)
12 Tradesman is no longer batting with tradesman (9)
13 Points obtained either side of court make one faint (5)
14 City of cities if it lost its capital (6)
15 Ruler given about one million for part of army (8)
18 The scientist is a very unpleasant fellow, cutting up mice (8)
20 A negative in time that is standing for hopeless mess (6)
23 Release shortly (5)
25 One who preserves the meat in an animal (9)
26 Marx on cause of death (7)
27 Where animals can get across? (7)
28 Scholarship for man of letters? (14)

DOWN

2 One who makes modifications would be more suitable without publicity (7)
3 Certain it has become complex (9)
4 To this part of where town ends (6)
5 Film which shows there is dancing everywhere? (8)
6 Complains, putting a note on the vehicle (5)
7 Something ugly climbed up into view (7)
8 Succeeded in getting a degree? (6,3,5)
9 Things that mark time and jump in store (6-4,4)
16 Like an egg in hotels: it makes a change (9)
17 Means of covering complaints? (8)
19 Falls for a new version of red aims (7)
21 Spoil the company in turning up as an inventor (7)
22 Something for the garden with water in the middle (6)
24 Means of cleaning second-class accommodation (5)

41

ACROSS

1 Drink outside and attract attention (5,3)
5 The end of a sentence or "time" (6)
9 A person looking for quarters – a toxophilite (8)
10 Heavenly fish! (6)
12 The viewer needs it for relaxation (6)
13 A window with a vista of the sea (8)
15 Made a resounding comeback (12)
18 Valuable growth for tea blenders (2,5,5)
23 Even mislead a good man, a compulsive worker (8)
24 Stand by English poet (6)
26 The girl left carrying a book (6)
27 Contribute about a thousand and one will get control (8)
28 Untidy appearance may be due to lack of clothing (6)
29 Stir a dish of oatmeal (8)

DOWN

1 Relationship between matron and nurse (6)
2 Article badly made – a sort of wreath (6)
3 Row following last month's failure (7)
4 A little pause does the trick, and that's not new (4)
6 He's put out when a point's awarded to the winner (7)
7 A coin – the form is quite rudimentary (8)
8 Increases the underworld watches closely (8)
11 This would be a record of course (3-4)
14 Taking it easy, being hurt yet again (7)
16 Driving instructors? (8)
17 Struggled, so gained converts (8)
19 Pull out, having added weight (7)
20 Blunder into someone fastening up a dog (7)
21 Timid fellow taking care of a minor (6)
22 American patriot always surrounded by soldiers (6)
25 Getting cut-up over nothing, though game (4)

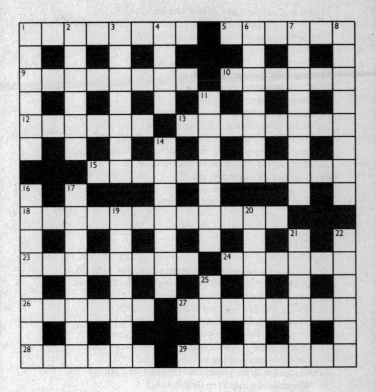

42

ACROSS

1 It's a sparkling wine – like it sent back? (4)
3 There's greater than usual concern about savage writer (5,5)
10 Once lines might be given for cheek (9)
11 Help to keep in credit – sharp! (5)
12 Pole in space, a scene of much action (5)
13 Bear allowed little water (8)
15 Going two ways for the top man (7)
17 Dropping back in the main (3-4)
19 Rants about article opposing destructive action (7)
21 At one time alluded to as impassioned (7)
22 No amateur joiner could be more extravagant (8)
24 Despicable guy having excellent backing in court (5)
27 Many an old church leader is a big noise (5)
28 He seldom looks in himself (9)
29 Pay attention or get the sack! (4,6)
30 Note written by a listener in dismay (4)

DOWN

1 Following a take-over the directors were real swine (6,4)
2 Discrimination shown – but not very much (5)
4 Decline to hold with second-rate means of defence (7)
5 Giving people a rise, one makes a bloomer! (7)
6 Western journalist responsible for a strike (5)
7 Such a law-breaker, it's clear, isn't reformable (9)
8 Getting some dividend, seldom objects (4)
9 Quietly taking first place is appealing! (8)
14 He deals with the young when the dams are skittish (10)
16 Where sailing men keep their cash? (5-4)
18 Chirpy response of second bird (8)
20 Think perhaps American coppers should go in a group (7)
21 Vagrant, a jerk after rare accommodation (7)
23 Shady character making the cigarette popular (5)
25 About to appear before the first woman magistrate (5)
26 Good man put out of business – a Northerner (4)

43

ACROSS

4 Having regard to programme for resort (8)
8 Flighty creature with money in bag (6)
9 Getting around ten points possibly just for standing (8)
10 A man of some authority in time taking over normally (8)
11 He'll bring many craft in (6)
12 Academic bosses must admit financial liability (8)
13 They are dependent on hearing devices (8)
16 Stealing off to see an old-fashioned doctor (8)
19 A sweet drink (soft) that is offered around very quietly (5,3)
21 The people count – that's official! (6)
23 King Edmund's press team (8)
24 Involved later in court battle (8)
25 Wanted to finish without challenge (6)
26 Not supported, so unsettled (8)

DOWN

1 Backchat evincing spite or otherwise? (7)
2 This is beneath 22, which is rare (9)
3 Strong liquor gives a tingle, nothing more (6)
4 Rips aren't seen to – make complaints (15)
5 Note the residue only is material (8)
6 Both articulate and thorough (5)
7 Hoarding gold in smart environment (7)
14 Extreme, even in its amended version (9)
15 The underworld have the answer – vanish! (8)
17 State date of birth as usual (7)
18 Clement the Marxist could appear congenial (7)
20 Meet and stay with royal characters (6)
22 A writer found lying in the street more dead than alive (5)

44

ACROSS

4 Viewing as a person without reserve (9)
8 Pick up serving men too – about a hundred (7)
9 A root vegetable it's normal to trim (7)
10 Greek character in charge filling in blundering moron (7)
11 One might well blow up and so spoil a great comeback (9)
13 A way to get around town, daring or otherwise (4-4)
14 The Italian holding back listening devices for this country (6)
17 Oriental movement occasioning strong feeling (7)
19 Uncompromising article – subject matter bones (6)
23 A hint (plain one!) (8)
25 Stuff being dear, get agitated (9)
26 Have further misgivings over the defence (7)
27 Makes an entry, a supplementary note about fruit (7)
28 Like junior going to pieces (7)
29 The staff loner pens odd letters (9)

DOWN

1 Maintenance-men on the offensive? (9)
2 An animal can hide if disturbed (7)
3 Box maybe, being perpetually gullible (9)
4 A girl will take part in some degree (6)
5 Music man speaking on ''X'' (8)
6 Melancholy pilgrim's greatest enemy (7)
7 Unpleasant row about honour (7)
12 Tied in knots, no-one raised the issue (7)
15 Caught suspect – and beat it! (5-4)
16 A tale of romance or nothing? (4-5)
18 Chinese official causing harm outside and in (8)
20 Crush tribal leaders with large following (7)
21 Adverts about English jackets (7)
22 Get involved and tour the building (7)
24 A little cavern always most spectacular in spring (6)

45

ACROSS

1 Church music composed by sincere church worker (10)
8 Lines right for the river (4)
10 An exchange of words isn't a solution for the Lower House! (10)
11 Like the individual with a large area of land (4)
13 A person colouring rope (7)
15 Find room for a vehicle about 45 inches long (6)
16 There's competition, note, to raise such a flower (6)
17 A right heel! (4,2,9)
18 A man of the cloth went first, and that's not good (6)
20 Come back and enlist again (6)
21 Pressed for a letting off (7)
22 Repeat a section of the chorus (4)
25 Appeals with an attempt to make a joke of it (10)
26 Venomous creatures quietly getting in dope (4)
27 Playing a role isn't a requirement of a politician (10)

DOWN

2 A woman put down about five hundred (4)
3 State ten was two-thirds (4)
4 He'll take the lead – but not on his own (2-4)
5 Converts sat in a gathering, by no means from choice (7,3,5)
6 13 across could be such a twister! (6)
7 Prepare an old fellow for great conflict (10)
9 Reckless men speed crazily on bad roads (10)
12 A restrictive practice that won't attract customers (6,4)
13 Chaucer's hen not fully occupied? (7)
14 Walker may well be up the pole! (7)
15 Pledge to invest money by and by in solid fuel (10)
19 Bores the doctor with complaints (6)
20 Spread about no more (6)
23 Make a move to supply porridge (4)
24 A number may be attached to any wild bird (4)

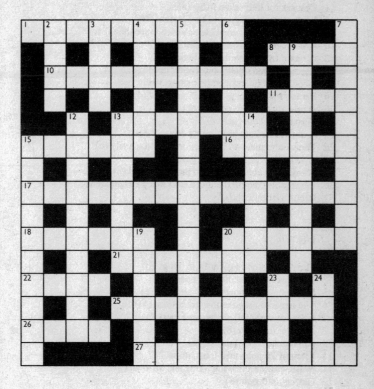

ACROSS

1 Charges for individual fruits (8)
5 Slight depression caused by 17, right? (6)
9 Rail on at lawless characters, which is sensible (8)
10 A ship carrying wine or bricks (6)
12 Hit hard by an advertising jingle (6)
13 Recognise and quietly receive eccentric (8)
15 It could be a mistake embellishing 30 (7)
16 Hector's piece about American capital (4)
20 A row growing out of control (4)
21 Turn cold on the green (7)
25 A quarter had not paid, being dogged (8)
26 The painter made to live in works satisfactorily (6)
28 A girl who's popular – and grating with it! (6)
29 Many hems are uneven, and that's material (8)
30 Information required about a road in a pleasant area (6)
31 Put off retirement (6,2)

DOWN

1 The doctor stood up, far from happy (6)
2 The idea is to have not one over (6)
3 Engaging a lad, bore with disruption (8)
4 The Icelandic sagas show great spirit (4)
6 Look for the small change in a party (6)
7 A jacket for town (8)
8 Appreciates compliments (8)
11 Merit of French verse translation (7)
14 Music-maker receiving a ring and a crown (7)
17 Getting into gear (8)
18 Compromise to put a stop to outrage (8)
19 Youth-leader after a drink, having the wind up (8)
22 A European holds it to be courteous (6)
23 Protect key wetlands in divine setting (6)
24 Like to strip on rising from taking a nap (6)
27 Unable to move at speed (4)

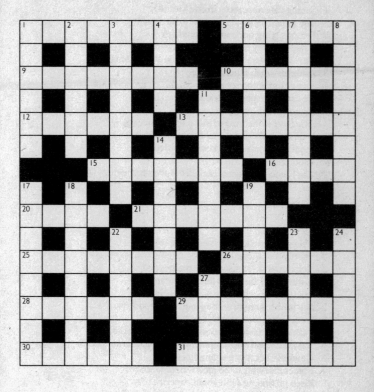

47

ACROSS

1 Seeing cannabis taken inside hurt (8)
5 The hound lay being injected with dope (6)
9 Persons lying quite unconsciously (8)
10 Raise possibly fifty in this country (6)
12 Cut about everything that grows in the garden (6)
13 A jogger when others are playing (8)
15 Accommodation for the unsociable chairman? (8,4)
18 He can make people lose all sense (12)
23 Figured stuff, pretty as can be (8)
24 After five is the time to make up the face (6)
26 Depressed about page to do with broadcast (6)
27 Produced original work when settled (8)
28 Snooping and on edge (6)
29 The French supporter backed the switch, the dog! (8)

DOWN

1 This plant can make a mess, note (6)
2 Plainly just accepting fitness training (6)
3 Help too ill-organised to be really good (3-4)
4 A minor machine part that's standard (4)
6 Thought like a pressman after all (7)
7 Got going without money and caused surprise (8)
8 Stand, strange to relate (8)
11 Talk about the unit opposing the ordinary soldier (7)
14 Support beastly development in the Mediterranean (7)
16 Quiet worker, but a champion (8)
17 Forces carrying some means of defence (8)
19 Keep on finding fault about America (7)
20 The guy in charge of the ship bearing fish (7)
21 Both right and wrong ideas may be put forward (6)
22 Make a bid, being soft (6)
25 Girl keeping company with a painter (4)

48

ACROSS

1 Check out note written by holy man (4)
3 Place with a railway still (10)
10 A clever person carries more change and notes (9)
11 Disastrous result of giving stout to a learner-driver (5)
12 Pitchers some viewers love watching (5)
13 Grass for interior decoration? (3-5)
15 Object after the French return a parliament (7)
17 Let off about fifty with a certain nonchalance (7)
19 Runs possibly ten cars (7)
21 An individual demanding cut-back and about to start ranting (7)
22 Stick around because it's light (8)
24 The dance of a medicine man in South Africa (5)
27 Soft grain, that's the penalty to be paid (5)
28 To inform about the élite is squealing (9)
29 Calm, and sees its effect (10)
30 Drove a fellow a little way (4)

DOWN

1 Ill-humour can upset Oriental self-restraint (10)
2 Running water – there are some without – a large number (5)
4 A guy's attachment for the outdoor life (4-3)
5 The double-dealer's art, or it could be (7)
6 Refuse a king left behind (5)
7 A sober worker accepts the consequence associated (9)
8 Cry for the bygone record (4)
9 Original spirit transforming the Tyneside area (8)
14 Sorted out – not for the first time! (10)
16 Brown is interrupting a story just to provoke (9)
18 He did a sound job in the main (8)
20 Comes down on a member of the family (7)
21 Out of wrongs make wrings (7)
23 Polish newspaper leader about half of the human race (5)
25 One must be wrapped in extra material of a particular kind (5)
26 Emulates the leaders of any party – especially socialist (4)

49

ACROSS

4 His stock is very small – should grow though (8)
8 Road transport driver (6)
9 The plant when alive ran wild (8)
10 Jam to use sparingly (8)
11 Serving men with some pretensions live here (6)
12 Held in affection (8)
13 Jumbo plane, the new sort (8)
16 3 has to tear around always (8)
19 Country people – swinish breed! (8)
21 Being brilliant makes Jack idle (6)
23 Giving the chop, yet remains in support (8)
24 Settled period – it unsettled men of letters (8)
25 Immature creatures, but they may well become high-fliers (6)
26 Without capital, and that's no life! (8)

DOWN

1 Changes having to do with classes (7)
2 Lying when writing about sharp rise (9)
3 16's circle – odd characters (6)
4 Fatal errors, every one (5,6,4)
5 A stretcher for use in the dark (8)
6 Given direction, scraps catalogues (5)
7 A restriction put on leave (7)
14 Whoever wore such a thing would certainly be sorry (4-5)
15 Refuse a seamstress overtime (8)
17 The current recession (3-4)
18 Maltreating lads can bring discredit (7)
20 Almost never start too soon (6)
22 Nowadays housing people better (5)

50

4 Feeling new plan should include space for outdoor living (9)
8 The serving men bearing with a woman (7)
9 Many came down quite exhausted (7)
10 Fitting a support – larger than normal (7)
11 Substitute, to put it mildly! (9)
13 Colour but comply if committed to prison (3-5)
14 Store fat with some hesitation (6)
17 Agrees to have everything invested in bonds (7)
19 Driven to collapse dead-drunk (6)
23 Sailing men in the union drink (8)
25 Inaction in disorder – a real bloomer (9)
26 To plant for kitchen use (7)
27 Discourtesy backed by far from pleasant traveller (7)
28 Decide upon artist to portray Greek heroine (7)
29 He claims there's little money about to hand over (9)

DOWN

1 Strong binding (9)
2 Means of quelling riots that's enough to make grown men weep (4-3)
3 Restless speed, crazy speed (9)
4 Not at one's best when getting into parking spot (6)
5 It's light in sea-going craft (8)
6 A German place accommodating two thousand is better kept (7)
7 Pilot through episcopal responsibility (7)
12 Relation – an odious word! (7)
15 Letters written as a priest maybe (9)
16 Pays attention in actual practice (9)
18 A job for the summer (8)
20 A great player – one filling up a hungry boy (7)
21 The medico should allow for a shortage of water (7)
22 Order the construction to be set taut (7)
24 Beat a guy on the baseball field (6)

51

ACROSS

1 He understands what others are thinking in spite of being pedestrian (7-6)
10 Punished after nude display although not seen clearly (9)
11 Woman who is back in hot water (5)
12 Payment for Ulysses (5)
13 Onlooker makes one stop and react badly (9)
14 Peer in racket producing source of light (4-4)
16 The office needs water after the polish has been put back (6)
19 Gains roughly about a second to hand out (6)
20 Corporal punishment a reactionary move? (8)
22 Make a noise like water circulating in a net (9)
24 Bouquet for a lady (5)
25 Bumper number? (5)
26 Deputy who could make ours great (9)
27 School-book about a suffragette possibly losing her head to become a leading politician (5,8)

DOWN

2 Retreats which show there is method in hot-headed plans (9)
3 No good for service, being a little feminine in the group (5)
4 Good-looking sailors love me (8)
5 Whichever way you look at it, it's bloodier (6)
6 Being amazed, we stopped work at the beginning of the afternoon (9)
7 Order to prepare for publication about a hundred (5)
8 Signs of discontent when barbarian structures include source of disease (6,7)
9 Ways in which a doubtful person goes without coarse food (13)
15 In revision for oral might encounter a mathematical term (9)
17 Vanish, leaving a girl to talk foolishly about love (9)
18 Run a cold mixture in a boiling vessel (8)
21 Give the old lady a slice of cake back: it will do her good (6)
23 Fast runner appearing in prestige race (5)
24 When dandies are about fifty they become failures (5)

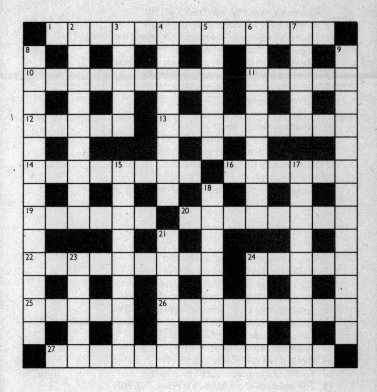

52

ACROSS

1 Go over a board that may be defied (10)
8 A good man – one getting the drink! (4)
10 Changes in diet now a requisite throughout the country (10)
11 Expert artist backed by the church (4)
13 The person observing a quarter idle away their time (7)
15 Virtuous aspiration in a certain class (6)
16 Strengthen a river enclosure (6)
17 Union conveners (8,7)
18 A guy who's evil or bent (6)
20 See about game – sharp! (6)
21 Supposed to propose cutting the tall grass (7)
22 Put in order that's quite considerable (4)
25 Plant on a tip site possibly (10)
26 Out of gear (4)
27 People in a rocky situation sound harrowing (10)

DOWN

2 Grants to obtain ballpoints (4)
3 Gamble with a Greek character (4)
4 The company tore up letters in error (6)
5 He was arresting man in days gone by (3,6,6)
6 Finished after a top journalist went round (6)
7 Swindle involving stone building in attractive surroundings (10)
9 The piles made by pugilists? (10)
12 Just aiming to be blonde (4-6)
13 A composer composing in tears (7)
14 Touching spring produces a reaction (7)
15 The approach about defence is reassuring (10)
19 Account for the noise (6)
20 Strict minister's retirement in view (6)
23 Some artiste thinking to be retained (4)
24 Pop in, causing distress (4)

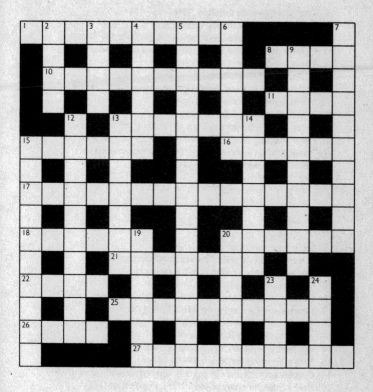

53

ACROSS

1 One's to appear in the show "Heaven" (8)
5 Ecclesiastic circle having difficulties (6)
9 Not for the first time, give out rule about dope (8)
10 Current publicity backing excellent area of Canada (6)
12 The draught that's really sickening (6)
13 O'Hara's red sports-shirt (8)
15 In the matter of louts, sense new determination (12)
18 When depressed they speed up (12)
23 A person not suited for running (8)
24 Some men dread her eagerness to hold on (6)
26 For a wedding charge a pound – that's about right (6)
27 Terriers taken in the car play. This reduced vision (8)
28 Get ale ordered for a flighty youngster (6)
29 Hear about the hide? (8)

DOWN

1 Stout guy employed as a caretaker (6)
2 A farm-worker should be stern about training (6)
3 Undeterred by a sandbank in the river (7)
4 Wise gardeners may well raise this (4)
6 Cryptic clue: seamen (Oriental) get food grown for cows (7)
7 Heartless rogue held to be rehabilitated (8)
8 Correct its fault in the hunt (8)
11 A number even make excuses (7)
14 Get husky beast to carry article one way (7)
16 Step taken over fur which is only fair (8)
17 Carol accepts cereals in general, though showing disdain (8)
19 Feel a little uncertain about silver and green stuff (7)
20 Carry on without help in retirement, appearing happy (7)
21 The French entry is representative (6)
22 Fruit produce for the jam firm (6)
25 Chinese meals? (4)

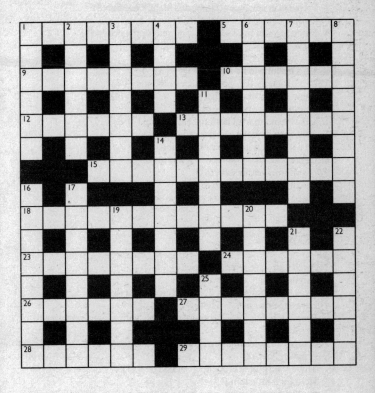

54

ACROSS

1 Prepares in advance – far more's plainly needed (8)
5 Cash pocketed by old chief (6)
9 Produce notes repeatedly as required for the prison (8)
10 A poet will have to endure direction (6)
12 Wickedly lively broadcast (6)
13 He's burning to be a baddie! (8)
15 Drink increased in price – such a bloomer (3-4)
16 Some speech or other that evokes memories (4)
20 Smooth and very strong (4)
21 Take the main road back to beat hold up (7)
25 Set a time to make calculations (8)
26 Fit a support with evident hesitation (6)
28 Depressed since confined to a bed (6) ...
29 ... suffering and in pain (8)
30 Quietly speak for a club (6)
31 Money received from the principal source (8)

DOWN

1 American song-writer's nurse (6)
2 Directed police offensive (6)
3 He'd disregard a rating doing the crossword (8)
4 Language that makes a fellow cross (4)
6 People looking for some sport catch this with a line – no trap will be used (6)
7 A top man holds nothing against the department (8)
8 A put-up job! (8)
11 Town transport is brought up a good deal (7)
14 Help for a little thing (7)
17 Sacked a representative for being explosive (8)
18 Make a reduction and it's a bargain! (8)
19 Charm will ensure entry (8)
22 That's about a thousand exercise – and five hundred just get in the way (6)
23 Join with a party-leader in division (6)
24 Full of promise as a reformer (6)
27 Note accommodation offered in a school (4)

55

ACROSS

1 A large amount of wood (4)
3 To study technique shows good sense (10)
10 Thwart the dissemination of news to all (9)
11 The council's involved Virginia in the row (5)
12 A measure taken by a sovereign (5)
13 Nomination in brief (8)
15 Boards can make the connection (7)
17 Stone jar with nickel lining (7)
19 Just one LP is the making of a Greek character (7)
21 He'll charge a consumer about a couple of hundred (7)
22 The new resident popped in (8)
24 A quarter accepted, though pale (5)
27 The current meaning (5)
28 Down town there's a bar with game (9)
29 An individual who doesn't work well enough (10)
30 Where those in the forces may eat hash (4)

DOWN

1 Worried by the lack of locks? (10)
2 An island everyone gets around to (5)
4 Causing a riot maybe on giving a speech (7)
5 Preserving a high tone, give voice about it (7)
6 A lemur kept in a cylindrical cage (5)
7 Unusual articles to bind into books (9)
8 Egghead backing up worker may effect a breakthrough (4)
9 Appearing genuine about proportional representation is just counteraction (8)
14 Dogs recovering in a country environment (10)
16 Cardinal's letter in French – it turned the French back (9)
18 Any crest used to show lineage (8)
20 Unskilled, yet quite outstanding (7)
21 Rather slow with neat solution (7)
23 Munched at to occupy the evening (5)
25 Confused minister cutting the drink (5)
26 Key to a hold-up in the Netherlands (4)

56

ACROSS

1 There is danger in swift preparation of drugs (8)
5 Rates at which the southern seas recede (6)
9 Being slovenly, has an accident with a tool (8)
10 More ideal (6)
12 Warm up in the fire he attempts to light (6)
13 Attention from journalists when there is a bit of a game in prison (8)
15 Agonising tendency in the audience (5-7)
18 She was one of his subjects (5,7)
23 Knight who makes one count up foreign arms (8)
24 If it went left instead of right there would be a place for this fabric (6)
26 Curious activities hostile to the civil service (6)
27 There is no point in feminine usefulness (8)
28 Last instalment put in to spend in good time (8)
29 Born brighter, he is an irritating person (8)

DOWN

1 Something to eat as a result of the old man's effort (6)
2 Get off with a flame (6)
3 To bet on the motorway is wrong (7)
4 Shut up shop (4)
6 Caress a bird acting as a model (7)
7 Expressive quote written up about a politician with reduced cover (8)
8 A very good scene changes, so clean the streets (8)
11 Storm after a low where the boats are found (7)
14 Lots of craft needed for getting a woman into one's embrace (7)
16 Supply water although furious about a swindle (8)
17 Fixed although honest at heart (8)
19 Reproduce design of image in river (7)
20 Forming the right conclusion but tearing it up? (7)
21 Stupid person about to compete for the council (6)
22 Tom and you appearing in different wars (6)
25 Island to ponder (4)

57

ACROSS

1 Many on the team make allowances, it's thought (13)
10 The top man's style is what he'll be remembered by (9)
11 Manage without a complaint (5)
12 Silver taken in before becoming a bore (5)
13 Dwell on people filling in at the game (9)
14 Half of them lament involvement in a Swiss place (8)
16 Free with money (6)
19 Flying without direction, get protection of sorts (6)
20 French article on the subject of a boy's lack of sense (8)
22 Part after a grim break-up and lengthy talk (9)
24 Feature a table-setting? (5)
25 In the clinic heat-treatment is provided in the recess (5)
26 The archbishop's formal at one and all almost (9)
27 For hours nice gals may be probing their inner selves (4-9)

DOWN

2 Colourful guy supporting William (9)
3 The woman making petition is retrogressive at heart (5)
4 Scenes of theatrical entertainment around ten (8)
5 A monkey rushes all over the place (6)
6 Restrained, but with some irascibility scoffed (9)
7 The weight of a cat (5)
8 The sole service generally available (4-9)
9 Oriental coppers stretch a point and agree warmly (13)
15 A person without equal. That could be put no plainer! (9)
17 Mistrust, though not very much (9)
18 The front – or near it anyway (8)
21 A brace can be left in the car (6)
23 Note the City put paid to this little beast (5)
24 Given credit, refuse to fail in business (5)

58

ACROSS

4 It's clear – even very clear this application (9)
8 Put to flight in the Orient as a matter of course (7)
9 A flat high up (7)
10 Suggests troublesome children have lie in (7)
11 Supervision could be a mistake (9)
13 The singer's a Brit – nasty individual (8)
14 Parking's to be found in a source of plants and shoots (6)
17 Free to let again (7)
19 Wet article written by politician in retreat (6)
23 Get a lift here – but expect to be down to earth later! (8)
25 Quite possibly a man's in it for keeps (9)
26 Savoury food seldom served? Not much! (7)
27 There's money but little company when old (7)
28 Get on board in the mdidle of a violent rainstorm (7)
29 Adjudicates in actual practice (9)

DOWN

1 Drill-set for certain soldiers (5-4)
2 Back up in fun (7)
3 Lilliputian art-work? (9)
4 Respecting a boy's sound mind (6)
5 Green growth in the main giving rise to less rage (8)
6 A way to sit a horse – a way to sit a horse (7)
7 A swimmer admits distress when so directed (7)
12 An old serving man opposed to summer in France did a runner (7)
15 Head receiving royal letters in support of a bore (9)
16 One stands perhaps to gain from such building material (9)
18 Risk with the aim to outrage (8)
20 Rating separate shellfish (7)
21 Coppers must accept an imposed punishment (7)
22 European bears in deplorable state (7)
24 This country is right, turning over grassland (6)

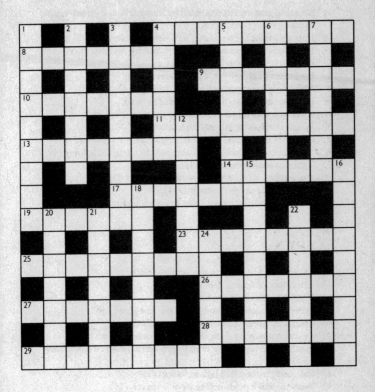

59

ACROSS

1 Sound of admiration produced by funny fellow without a game (4-7)
9 Helen's mother appears in a pale damask robe (4)
10 He sounds like a pacifist but is not paid for his time (5-6)
11 Letter left for a man (4)
14 Bachelors I capture – it's the headgear! (7)
16 Make holy greetings before Whitsun starts (6)
17 Illustrate again two things meat might be (6)
18 A service which brings ecstasy to the people? (6,9)
19 Wager one has turned into an insect (6)
21 Converse fondly and go to bed, but he has to work hard (6)
22 Without endless affliction a man is not among the leaders (4-3)
23 Time for something to eat (4)
26 Show relative includes the north as source (11)
27 Play the instrument backwards (4)
28 Two chaps and I give voice in a condescending manner (11)

DOWN

2 There would be a row if this god lost his head (4)
3 Effrontery of female winner (4)
4 Fruit served twice for a Lord (6)
5 Weapon for one who turns after the first shot (7,8)
6 Colour up after a story is put into songs (6)
7 To catch a woman right in the open country is hell (6,5)
8 Godhead permits something to grow as a means of suspension (7-4)
12 Pale and pinched as Thomas looks (11)
13 Working out a point before a party speech (11)
14 Where I toss up on the way (7)
15 In their excitement a number go wrong about love (7)
20 Woman who lets a liar go free (6)
21 Against holding a woman as a weapon (6)
24 Information from all quarters (4)
25 Figure I study (4)

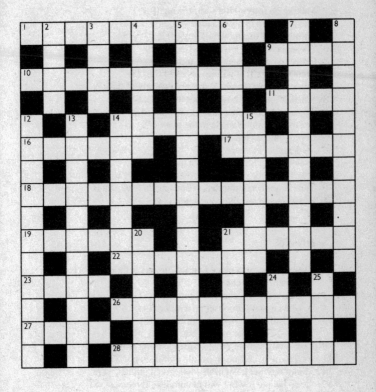

60

ACROSS

1 Making an impression – so striking (8)
5 The firm with many graduates stops short (6)
9 Fitting pipes to a new building (8)
10 These days a bog engenders respect (6)
12 Grace has got in with a liar, unfortunately (6)
13 A catastrophe that will involve sad rites (8)
15 Fly around buffet where there's a variety of fish (7)
18 Smirk if spirit is shown about the Right (4)
20 The university may end beer supplies (4)
21 See main changes made in the plant (7)
25 Left, being unpleasant (8)
26 Stick a man in the centre (6)
28 Collect articles received by a monarch (6)
29 A large number put inside break free – such an adventure! (8)
30 Temporary accommodation housing an occupant (6)
31 Produces the family – is on guard (8)

DOWN

1 Keeping a pet in a place fit only for pigs is thoughtless (6)
2 A copper ring or charm (6)
3 Artistic work it's cheap to reproduce (8)
4 A well-known school set up a record (4)
6 Trial resulting from gold transaction (6)
7 The medico is true maybe, but wet (8)
8 Makes notes about erosion, using strong language (8)
11 As a trailblazer, one wants all-round support (7)
14 Mount without hesitation when given guidance (7)
17 Sense people rowing will encompass agreement (8)
18 The board put on weight, due to copious seafood (8)
19 Youngster holding a certain Greek character to be an awful beast (8)
22 Like a high-flier getting behind (6)
23 Pass comment about the objective (6)
24 A river always going in different directions (6)
27 Land backing up the Spanish Italian agreement (4)

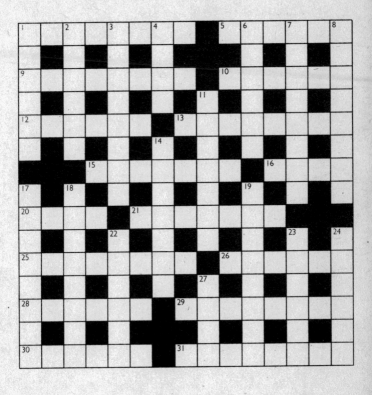

No.1

No.2

No.3

No.4

162

No.5

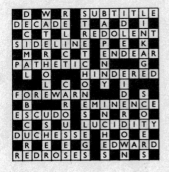

	F		S		I	N	S	U	L	A	T	E
C	A	R	N	E	T		E		I		A	
	I		C		A		S	E	D	I	M	E	N	T
F	R	O	U	F	R	O	U		A		I		T
	W		R		C		R		T	I	T	I	A	N
B	A	R	A	T	H	E	A		I		R	
	Y		B			N	O	V	E	L	L	A	S
			L		P		C		E		A	
C	O	V	E	R	A	G	E		U		I	
	U		T		O		U		T		
S	T	A	R	V	E		P	O	L	Y	G	A	M	Y
	C		E		N		L	E	T	H	A	R	G	Y
C	O	N	F	E	T	T	I		O		B		I
	M		I		E		C		F	E	L	O	N	Y
L	E	A	T	H	E	R	Y		F		E		E

No.6

M	O	R	A	S	S	E	S		I	M	A	G	E	S
E		E		U		A		A		A		W
R	E	A	R	M	O	S	T		E	L	V	I	R	A
L		L		P		E		C		A		N
I	N	T	O	T	O		A	R	M	R	E	S	T	S
N		Y		E		B		O		I		A		O
			A	R	T	I	C	U	L	A	T	I	O	N
A		M			S		T			D		G
S	H	A	R	P	S	H	O	O	T	E	R	
S		D		E		O		N		R	R		B
E	A	R	D	R	O	P	S		C	I	N	E	M	A
M		I		C		S		S		T		F		D
B	E	G	G	A	R		S	T	A	R	T	I	N	G
L		A		L			Y	E		L		E
Y	O	L	K	E	D		R	E	T	A	I	L	E	R

No.7

	D		W		R		S	U	B	T	I	T	L	E
D	E	C	A	D	E		T		A		D		I
	C		T		L		R	E	D	O	L	E	N	T
S	I	D	E	L	I	N	E		P		E		K
	M		R		C		T		E	N	D	E	A	R
P	A	T	H	E	T	I	C		N		G	
	L		O			H	I	N	D	E	R	E	D
			L		C		O		Y		I	
F	O	R	E	W	A	R	N			D		S
	B			R		E	M	I	N	E	N	C	E
E	S	C	U	D	O		S		N		R		O
	C		S		U		L	U	C	I	D	I	T	Y
D	U	C	H	E	S	S	E		H		O		E
	R		E		E		G		E	D	W	A	R	D
R	E	D	R	O	S	E	S		S		N		S

No.8

D	O	L	D	R	U	M	S		S	K	I	R	U	N
O		I		E		I			U		A		O
C	O	N	D	E	N	S	E		A	D	A	G	I	O
T		T		D		D		R		Z		G		N
O	N	E	U	P		E	M	O	L	U	M	E	N	T
R		L		I		M		A			D		I
	S	P	R	E	A	D	E	A	G	L	E	D	
S		U		E		A		S		N		Y		E
T	U	N	A	S	A	N	D	W	I	C	H	
R		S			O		E		E		S		P
I	N	T	E	R	L	U	D	E		S	U	E	D	E
D		A		A		R		P		T		R		N
E	M	B	R	Y	O		N	I	C	O	T	I	A	N
N		L		O			N		R		A		E
T	O	E	I	N	G		E	G	G	S	A	L	A	D

163

No.9

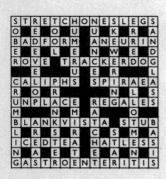

No.10

No.11

No.12

No.13

```
C U T E   M A T R I C I D A L
O   I   E   P   O   L   I   I
A N C E S T R A L   A R S O N
C   K   P   O   L   P   A   N
H O S T A   P R E S S U R E
T   L   O   R   M   S
R A B B I T S   S P A N I E L
I   O   E       N   N   E
P I T P R O P   F A T I G U E
S   H   E   L   I       P
  H E R B A R I A   H E A R T
S   R   A   S   T   E   X   I
O S I E R   I N C U R R I N G
L   N   O   S   A   O   O   H
O R G A N S T O P S   S M U T
```

No.14

```
M A I N D I S H   C A L P A C
O   S   I   O   B   E   H
D O O R P O S T   P A W N E E
E   B   L   O   T   D   T   A
S H A D O W   H E A D L A M P
T   R   M   E   R   O   G   E
      P A R S I M O N I O U S
A S   S   P   I   N   T
S A T I S F A C T O R Y
P   A   U   R   E   A   P   I
H U M A N I T Y   S P R I N G
O   P   L   O   E   H   N   N
D R O V E R   S A R A J E V O
E   U   S   S   E   R   R
L A T E S T   W E L L D O N E
```

No.15

No.16

165

No.17

```
L A S H   M E T A C A R P U S
O   L   C   A   M   G   A   U
W H I T H E R T O   A F T E R
E   N   A   A   U   T   A   E
R O G E R   C O N V E R G E
C       C   H   T       O   I
L E P R O S E   S T E R N U M
A   E   A       M   I       P
S E T T L E S   A G I T A T E
S   R       W   D   S       R
  G O A T H E R D   S A M O S
B   L   H   R   U   I   A   O
A B E L E   V I C T O R I A N
C   U   M   E   E   N   Z   A
H U M B E R S I D E   S E A L
```

No.18

```
  S   H   S   G U L L I V E R
M O S A I C   E   E   N   R
  M   R   A   R E A R L A M P
C A R D A M O M   T   E   I
  L   L   P   A   H A T I N G
D I V I S I O N   E   E   E
  S   N       S E R E N A D E
    E   E   H   Y   I
P R E S E N C E       G   S
  A       G   P R O P H E C Y
A M B L E R   H   N   T   A
  P   O   A   E G R E M O N T
P A S S O V E R   U   A   D
  G   E   E   D   S T R E A K
H E B R I D E S   H   E   L
```

No.19

```
P A N O R A M A   S T R E E T
A   O   I   E       O   T   R
R A I N C O A T   F U L C R A
I   S   H   N   B   R   H   I
T H E N A R   A L S A T I A N
Y   S   R   R   O   C   N   E
      A D D E R S T O N G U E
S   N       C       S   S
C O U N T R Y H O U S E
H   R   R   C   M   P   N   S
O B S T A C L E   L E G A T O
L   L   C   E   M   C   R   R
A L I G H T   W I N I F R E D
R   N   E       C   A   O   I
S I G N A L   H A L L O W E D
```

No.20

```
D   K   D   A N C H O R I T E
I N I T I A L   Y   E   H   H
S   P   S   K   A D A P T E R
C A L U M N Y       R   A   A
O   I   I   N E G O T I A T E
V A N I S H E D   S   N   R
E   G   S       I   K I T T E N
R       A B S T A I N       E
Y E A R L Y   O   C   E   U
  Y   A   P   R H E O S T A T
D E M I T A S S E   G   E   R
  B   L   S   A M N E S I A
P R O M I S E   D   I   I   L
  O   E   E       O U T F A L L
S W A N S D O W N   O   N   Y
```

No.21

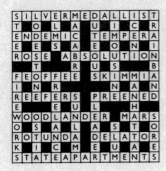

```
. F . C . A . P A S T O R A L
B I S H O P . R . U . R . B .
R . A . P . E N N O B L E D .
S E A M L E S S . D . I . Y .
. M . P . A . E . R A T T A N
R E T A I L E R . E . N . . .
. N . G . . V E S I C A T E .
. . . P . A . S . U . . . . .
C O V E N A N T . R . G . . .
U . . R . . I N V E I G L E .
A T T I L A . O . I . O . A .
L . S . M . N O A H S A R K .
V I R T U O S I . B . I . I .
N . L . U . S . L I T A N Y .
S E W E R R A T . E . Y . G .
```

No.22

```
S E M P S T R E S S . S P A R
O . A . T . E . H . R . O . O
M A N O R . F E U D A T O R Y
A . I . A . R . T . R . V . A
. P R I V A T E S C H O O L .
S . L . G . I . . H . K . F
E L E P H A N T . P I N E A L
L . T . S . F . M . . . . U
L A S C A R . B R E A T H E S
A . T . C . E . N . E . H
F I R S T O F F E N D E R
I . I . O . I . T . R . O . O
E S P E R A N T O . I V I E D
L . E . C . W . T . N . E
D A S H . C H A N G E L E S S
```

No.23

```
S I L V E R M E D A L L I S T
T . O . L . A . U . I . C . R
E N D E M I C . T E M P E R A
E . E . S . A . E . O . N . I
R O S E . A B S O L U T I O N
. T . . R . U . S . . . . B
F E O F F E E . S K I M M I A
I . N . R . . . N . A . N
R E E F E R S . P R E E N E D
E . . E . U . L . . . H
W O O D L A N D E R . M A R S
O . S . A . L . A . S . T . O
R O T U N D A . D E L A T O R
K . I . C . M . E . U . A . E
. S T A T E A P A R T M E N T S
```

No.24

```
. S Q U A S H C O U R T .
P . U . R . E . I . O . S . M
E M I T S . C O N S O R T I A
R . T . E . T . T . R . I
M I S I N F O R M . A V O I D
A . I . R . E . G . N . E
N O T I C E . U N B E A T E N
E . R . T . T . . . I . C
N E A T H E R D . S C R A P E
T . V . E . I . P . A . N
W H E A T . F I R E L I G H T
A . R . A . F . E . O . U . U
V E S T I G I A L . M I S E R
E . E . R . D . I . E . T . Y
. M A R S H M A L L O W .
```

No.27 **No.28**

No.25

```
G O O D S T R A I N ▮ ▮ ▮ ▮ N
▮ P ▮ O ▮ E ▮ L ▮ A ▮ O P I E
A N N U N C I A T E ▮ E ▮ ▮ W
▮ L ▮ S ▮ U ▮ T ▮ I ▮ I R I S
▮ T ▮ O R A T I O N ▮ S ▮ ▮ V
S T R I V E ▮ L ▮ N O V I C E
E ▮ A ▮ E ▮ ▮ T ▮ ▮ S ▮ ▮ N
C E N T R A L L Y H E A T E D
O ▮ S ▮ T ▮ ▮ E ▮ P ▮ E ▮ O
N O V E L S ▮ A ▮ B A N N E R
D ▮ E ▮ Y E A R N E D ▮ ▮ T
H A R E ▮ C ▮ N ▮ R ▮ S ▮ H
A ▮ S ▮ S T R I P T E A S E
N E E D ▮ O ▮ N ▮ H ▮ G ▮ R
D ▮ ▮ ▮ R I G M A R O L E S
```

No.26

```
S T A C C A T O ▮ D A N I S H
O ▮ L ▮ O ▮ I ▮ W ▮ G ▮ A
L A M E N T E R ▮ C A N N O N
E ▮ O ▮ T ▮ R ▮ G ▮ K ▮ I ▮ D
L E S S E E ▮ M E D I A T E S
Y ▮ T ▮ N ▮ A ▮ N ▮ N ▮ I ▮ O
▮ ▮ ▮ S T A N D I N G R O O M
S ▮ A ▮ T ▮ S ▮ N ▮ ▮ E
M A G N E T I C T A P E ▮ ▮
O ▮ E ▮ X ▮ Q ▮ A ▮ R ▮ S ▮ G
C O N S T R U E ▮ P I R A T E
K ▮ C ▮ R ▮ E ▮ B ▮ M ▮ V ▮ N
I R I S E S ▮ P L E A S A N T
N ▮ E ▮ M ▮ ▮ U ▮ T ▮ N ▮ R
G A S K E T ▮ R E C E N T L Y
```

No.27

```
W A R D R E S S ▮ L O O F A H
E ▮ E ▮ A ▮ T ▮ E ▮ B ▮ L ▮ A
A T R O P H I E S ▮ L E A R N
T ▮ U ▮ E ▮ F ▮ U ▮ A ▮ G ▮ S
H U N T S ▮ F O R E T A S T E
E ▮ E ▮ ▮ I ▮ E ▮ T ▮ L
R E T R E N C H E D ▮ S A G A
B ▮ H ▮ D ▮ H ▮ N ▮ I ▮ F ▮ N
O V E R ▮ E I S T E D D F O D
A ▮ R ▮ U ▮ P ▮ E ▮ ▮ G
R E M I N I S C E ▮ O F F E R
D ▮ I ▮ I ▮ H ▮ X ▮ G ▮ L ▮ E
I N D U S ▮ O U T E R M O S T
N ▮ O ▮ O ▮ T ▮ R ▮ A ▮ U ▮ E
G E R U N D ▮ B A L M O R A L
```

No.28

```
▮ C ▮ S ▮ N ▮ O V E R S E A S
T A T T O O ▮ R ▮ P ▮ E ▮ R
▮ Y ▮ A ▮ G ▮ A L I E N A T E
P E N T A G O N ▮ D ▮ O ▮ I
▮ N ▮ I ▮ I ▮ G ▮ U N R E S T
A N N O U N C E ▮ R ▮ ▮ A
▮ E ▮ N ▮ ▮ F L A G G I N G
▮ ▮ ▮ E ▮ I ▮ R ▮ L ▮ A
E S T R A N G E ▮ ▮ B ▮ A
A ▮ ▮ S ▮ E V I D E N C E
S L I G H T ▮ S ▮ T ▮ R ▮ R
▮ T ▮ R ▮ A ▮ T E A R D R O P
H A C I E N D A ▮ L ▮ I ▮ B
N ▮ M ▮ C ▮ T ▮ I O N I A N
S T A M P E D E ▮ C ▮ E ▮ T
```

No.29

No.30

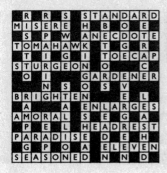

No.31

No.32

No.33

```
C L A S S E S   S E S T I N A
H   V   L   A   E   P   C   R
A D A M A N T   D I A R I S T
M   L   C   R   A   N   N   I
B L A N K C A R T R I D G E S
E   N     P   I   A       T
R E C I F E   O V E R S H O E
    H   L   L   E   D   E
C H E R O K E E   A S K A N T
A   W   G   A     R   O
B E T T E R A N D B E T T E R
I   I   R   L   V   L   F   M
N O T A B L E   E N L A R G E
E   H   E   S   N   E   E   N
T R E A D L E   T A N G E N T
```

No.34

```
D A S H   P R O P E R T I E S
E   N   C   A   I   I   M   O
E L E V A T I O N   A P P A L
P   E   R   L   N   N   R   E
L A R G O   I N A C T I O N
I     L   N   C     V     I
T E S T I N G   E M O T I O N
T   H   N     V   S   S
E M I N E N T   P R E T E X T
R   P   E   R   R     I
  A S P I R A T E   C L U N G
I   H   S   C   S   A   S   A
S T A L L   A S S I S T A N T
I   P   E   K   E   T   G   E
S H E E T B E N D S   N E S S
```

No.35

```
  R   C   L   A N A G R A M S
B E C O M E   L   N   A   A
  S   N   G   L A T I T U D E
R E S T R A I N   I   E   E
  R   I   T   I   M O S A I C
E V E N S O N G   O     R
  E   E     H A N D C L A P
    N   B   T   Y   A
A S H T R A Y S     R   S
  E     N   I M P U N I T Y
H A R O L D   T   E   A   E
  P   F   I   T O G E T H E R
C O N F E T T I   G   I   P
  R   E   T   N   E V O K E R
S T A R T I N G   D   N   R
```

No.36

```
C L O T H E S P E G       C
A   O   R   E   A   O S L O
C O N T A I N E R S   T   M
E   E   S   C   N   M A I M
  G   D E R I D E R   N   U
M A R A U D   L   T E N D O N
O   E   B     S   A   P   A
T H E W I T C H I N G H O U R
I   N   O   A     E   I   D
V A L O U R   R   A N A N A S
A   I   S U P P O R T   T
T O G A   S   E   C   F   M
I   H   C H I N C H I L L A
O A T H   E   E   E   E   M
N     S I R O R M A D A M
```

170

No.37

No.38

No.39

No.40

No.37

```
H A N D S O M E   S T R A P S
A   A   K   E     E   I   T
R E P A I R E D   A M E R C E
A   L   R   T   M   P   S   E
S H E A T H   D I R E C T O R
S   S   E   S   S   R   R   A
    A D U L T E R A T I N G
L   S     I   R     P   E
A N T H R O P O L O G Y
M   A   E   P   Y   A   P   A
B U L L A C E S   P L I A N T
A   L   L   D   B   A   N   R
S P I R I T   S U I T C A S E
T   N   S     L   E   M   S
S I G N E T   P L E A S A N T
```

No.38

```
A   R   S   O V E R I S S U E
S H A T T E R   O   H   N
S   M   R   D   P U R I T A N
A P P R I S E   L   F   I
I   A   A   A S S E N T E R S
L I G H T A L E   T   E   E
A   E   I   A   T I R A D E
N     O A R S M E N   X
T A L E N T   I   T   S   O
    N   X   H   D A L E S M A N
D I S P E L L E D   R   O   E
    M   R   E   H O L S T E R
M A J E S T Y   E   I   H   A
    T   S   E   R A N K E S T
H O R S E S H O E   E   R   E
```

No.39

```
R E C E I V E S   B A L L O T
E   H   N   V     M   E   O
D A U G H T E R   F O R M E R
D   M   E   N   U   O   R
E X P E R T   E M I N E N C E
R   S   E   S   E   T   A   N
    U N I C O R N   A D I T
B   D   T   R   S   S   E   S
L O R D   G A R O T T E
A   O   A   P   N   O   F   A
C O W S L I P S   S P R E A D
K   N   L   Y   F   P   D   H
O L I V E R   P I N A F O R E
U   N   G     N   G   R   R
T E G M E N   G E N E R A T E
```

No.40

```
V A N I S H I N G C R E A M
S   D   N   E   E   A   Y   A
E X A C T O R   W A R B E C K
C   P   R   E   S   P   S   I
O U T F I T T E R   S W O O N
N   E   C   O   E     R   G
D U R B A N   R E G I M E N T
H     T   B   L   N     H
A C A D E M I C   A N O M I E
N   D   N   C   O   A   G
D E M O B   D E L I V E R E R
S   I   R   I   O   A   C   A
H A R P O O N   C A T F O R D
O   E   O   G   H   E   N   E
P O S T M A S T E R S H I P
```

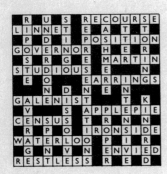

No.41

```
S T A N D O U T   P E R I O D
I   N   E     S     V   N   I
S E A R C H E R   P I S C E S
T   D   L   D   L   C   H   T
E Y E L I D   P O R T H O L E
R   M   N   R   G   O   A   N
    R E V E R B E R A T E D
C     A       S     O   E   S
O F G R E A T W O R T H
A   O   X   I   K   E   C   R
C O N S T A N T   B R O O K E
H   I   R   G   P   R   W   V
M I S S A L   D O M I N A T E
E   E   C     L     E   R   R
N U D I T Y   P O R R I D G E
```

No.42

```
A S T I   O S C A R W I L D E
N   A   P   A   N   H   A   N
I N S O L E N C E   A C R I D
M   T   E   D   M   C   C   S
A R E N A   B R O O K L E T
L       D   A   N     N   H
F O R K I N G   E B B T I D E
A   I   N         A   S   A
R A V A G E S   E X C I T E D
M   E   E   U   R   K   M
  P R O F U S E R   C U R I A
S   B   A   P   A   H   E   S
C L A N G   E X T R A V E R T
O   N   I   C   I   T   V   E
T A K E N O T I C E   F E A R
```

No.43

```
  R   U S   R E C O U R S E
L I N N E T   E   A   T   T
  P   D   I   P O S I T I O N
G O V E R N O R   H   E   R
  S   R   G   E   M A R T I N
S T U D I O U S   E   N
  E   O   N   E A R R I N G S
    N D N   E   N
G A L E N I S T   T   K
  V   S     A P P L E P I E
C E N S U S   T   R   N   N
  R   P   O   I R O N S I D E
W A T E R L O O   P   I   R
  G   N   V   N   E N V I E D
R E S T L E S S   R   D
```

No.44

```
A   E   E   B E H O L D I N G
R E C O V E R   R   E   O
M   H   E   E   P A R S N I P
O M I C R O N   T   P   S
U   D   G   D E T O N A T O R
R I N G R O A D   R   I   M
E   A   E   I   I S R A E L
R     E M O T I O N     O
S T E R N A   I   A   R   V
  R   E   N   O V E R T O N E
G A B E R D I N E   E   T   S
  M   F   A   R E D O U B T
A P P E A R S   N   R   N   O
  L   R   I   A S U N D E R
P E R S O N N E L   M   A   Y
```

No.45

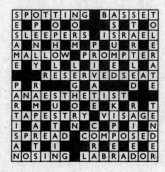

No.46

```
M A N D A T E S   S A U C E R
O   O   D   L     S   A   E
R A T I O N A L   S P O R T S
O   I   R   N   D   E   D   P
S L O G A N   P E R C E I V E
E   N   B   C   S   T   G   C
    B L O O M E R   B A I T
D   E   E   R   R   D   N   S
R A N K   C O N V E R T
E   D   P   N   E   A   D   A
S H A D O W E D   R U B E N S
S   N   L   T   F   G   F   L
I N G R I D   C A S H M E R E
N   E   T     S   T   N   E
G A R D E N   S T A Y E D U P
```

No.47

No.48

```
T E S T   S T A T I O N A R Y
E   O   P   E   R   F   T   E
M E M O R A N D A   F A T A L
P   M   I   T   I   A   E   P
E W E R S   P O T P L A N T
R     T   E   O     D   R
A L T H I N G   R E L E A S E
N   A   N     E   N   A
C A N T E R S   E X A C T O R
E   T     T   X   D     R
    C A S E M E N T   S A M B A
A   L   M   P   O   M   O   N
P R I C E   S C R E A M I N G
E   S   N   O   T   N   R   E
S T E A D I N E S S   H E R D
```

No.49

```
R P C     S E E D S M A N
P E T R O L   E   N O B
  F   O E V A L E R I A N
C O N S E R V E   A T N
  R   T I N R E S I D E
E M B R A C E D   G   O
  S   A   E L E P H A N T
      T   A R A
R E V E R E N D     I S
  B   W   L A N D R A C E
A B L A Z E   Y E S A
  T M R   S L A S H I N G
L I T E R A T I   R I D
  D N G N   L A R V A E
H E A D L E S S   Y T L
```

No.50

```
S T D   P A L P A T I O N
T H E R E S A   O   R V
R A   S   S D R A I N E D
A P R O P O S   T   M R
P   G   E U P H E M I S E
P E A G R E E N   O E E
I   S A   C L A R D E R
N   T A L L I E S   E
G O A D E D   E P S H
  L   R D A B S I N T H E
N I C O T I A N A R A A
V U T   T O A S T E R
P I L G R I M T T U S
E H O   E L E C T R A
P R E T E N D E R S E L
```

No.51

No.52

No.53

No.54

No.55

No.56

```
C O N S I D E R A T I O N
S   R   U   I   H   E   U   S
H E A D S T O N E   M A N G E
O   N   I   R   S   P   C   N
E A G R E   A M U S E M E N T
R   E       M   S   R       I
E M M E N T A L   R A N S O M
P   A   O   S   A   T   U   E
A W N I N G   U N R E A S O N
I   P   C   T       P   T
R I G M A R O L E   C H I N A
I   E   R   U   R   R   C   L
N I C H E   P R I M A T I A L
G   K   I   L   O   S   O   Y
  S O U L S E A R C H I N G
```

```
T   S   M   R E L E V A N C E
R O U T I N E   E   S   O
A   P   N   A   P L A T E A U
I M P L I E S   G   R   C
N   O   A   O V E R S I G H T
B A R I T O N E   A   D   E
A   T   U   T   S P E E D S
N   R E L E A S E   A
D A M P E N   R   R   S   N
  B   E   D   A I R F I E L D
M A I N T A I N S   O   R   S
  L   A   N   R A R E B I T
C O I N A G E   A   A   I   O
  N   C   E   E N T R A I N
R E H E A R S A L   E   N   E
```

```
W O L F W H I S T L E   N   G
  D   A   A   E   I   L E D A
P I E C E W O R K E R   T   L
  N   E   H   V   D   P H I L
C   E   B A S I N E T   E   O
H A L L O W   C   R E D R A W
I   A   L   E   N   W   S
P U B L I C T R A N S P O R T
P   O   V   E   I   R   R
E A R W I G   V   C O O L I E
N   A   A L S O R A N   D   E
D A T E   O   L   N   N   I
A   I   P R O V E N I E N C E
L O O T   I   E   O   W   O
E   N   P A T R O N I S I N G
```

```
S T A M P I N G   C O M M A S
C   P   A   O   R   O   W
A P P O S I T E   A D M I R E
T   E   T   E   P   E   S   A
T H A L I A   D I S A S T E R
Y   L   C   S   O   L   U   I
    W H I T I N G   G R I N
E   P   E   E   E   M   E   G
Y A L E   N E M E S I A
E   A   A   R   R   N   R   S
S I N I S T E R   C O H E R E
I   K   T   D   I   T   M   V
G A T H E R   E S C A P A D E
H   O   R   L   U   R   R
T E N A N T   B E A R S K I N
```